Shopping
for the
Real
You

10 Essential Steps
to a Better Wardrobe for
Every Woman: Fashionistas,
Fashion-phobes, and
the Over 50

Andrea Pflaumer

Ordering Information
To order additional copies go to:

ShoppingfortheRealYou.com

Illustrations: Susan Tait Porcaro, 2Lips Art & Design

Book design: Shannon Bodie, Lightbourne, Inc.

2nd Edition, April 2017

ISBN: 978-0-9708674-4-5 (Paperback)
ISBN: 978-0-9708674-5-2 (eBook)

Dedicated to my mother, Sadie,
and her favorite philosopher, Popeye,
who said: "I yam what I yam."

✤ ✤ ✤

Summer

Contents

Introduction

F ashion seems like one of the more trivial pursuits in life. But in fact what we wear is a potent and tangible expression of everything that we are: our individuality, our cultural identity, our taste.

For most of us, choosing the right clothing in the colors and styles that flatter our body and coloring is not an easy task, at least for me it wasn't for a long time. In fact, it's the very reason I wrote this book.

Since my childhood I'd had something of a love/hate relationship with fashion starting at the age of six when I discarded the outfits provided with my paper dolls and designed clothes that I would have preferred to wear. By my teens and early twenties I was sewing many of my clothes, knitting sweaters and even making some purses. But as I grew older free time became scarcer, and shopping became a never-ending struggle. I found it increasingly difficult to find items that were flattering to my face and body, suited to my personality and priced within my budget. I began to question my own judgment and ended up wasting a lot of time and money on clothes that were popular but unflattering.

All that began to change when I first heard about individual color analysis in the 1980s. Wanting to learn more about the subject, I made an appointment with a color consultant. After a lengthy analysis using four pre-set seasonal color fans, she informed me that I was a "spring." Although I never related to most of the colors in that color fan I became fascinated with the seasonal color concept...obsessed, in fact. I had to learn as much as I could about it.

What I learned was that over the past century, long before the seasonal color concept became popular, two women wrote extensively about individual color and style, raising both subjects to a high art. The first of these was Grace Margaret Morton. For more than thirty years Morton was the head of textiles and fashion at the University of Omaha. She explained how the Asian concepts of yin and yang, qualities in nature that express the extremes of dynamism and repose, correlate to an individual's bone structure, speech, behavior, coloring, and style.

Expanding on Morton's ideas Harriet McJimsey, professor of textiles at Iowa State University, wrote in great detail about the concept of what she termed color *harmony* and used the concept of yin and yang to specify an individual's style qualities. (I find it extremely interesting that these two women from the heartland of America had such profound insights about individual fashion and style and took their cues from the symbolism of the Far East.)

The third pioneer, Suzanne Caygill, was a San Francisco milliner and bon vivant, very likely inspired by Morton and McJimsey's work. Caygill codified a system of individual color typing based on what she saw in the eye, skin and hair coloring of her clients. Using a watercolor paint set she crafted finely tuned, individual color palettes that she correlated with the seasons of the year: winter, spring, summer and fall. Caygill taught design seminars and developed a color-related television program in the 1950s; she is widely regarded as the mother of modern color analysis. Her book *Color: The Essence of You* delineated several sub-categories of the four seasons to broaden the range and understanding of individual color typing. Although the book is now quite dated, her work became a jumping-off point for many contemporary color analysts and systems.

One who took that jump was Caygill's primary acolyte, Joan Songer, founder of Personal Style Counselors (PSC) in Oakland, California. And that's where I, finally and fortunately, landed.

A brilliant color consultant from Songer's office named John Kitchener—now director of PSC—taught me about my specific and unique color palette, a rather complex and challenging one at that, which explained my years of fashion frustration. I also learned about the style lines most flattering to my body and bone structure, which, as it turned out, were the very ones that I had longed for in my teens. Finally I felt vindicated...and validated. My early intuitions about the clothes I liked—even though often hard to find—were accurate.

And so, the purpose of this book is to share with you all that I have learned from my mentors. Although the information in this book applies to any age demographic, I've included a good amount of material for what I consider a widely neglected one, my own—women of a certain age. There comes a point in your life when you realize that much of what you see in catalogs, fashion magazines and the media no longer reflects who you are. Since we're all aging and, if we're fortunate, will be in this demographic eventually, it's a good idea to understand how to establish your unique identity early. Then you will be able to represent the real you throughout your lifetime, regardless of the whims of fashion.

Any individual chapter in this book will immediately help you improve your buying choices. But most people find that it takes time—often a few years—to transform an entire wardrobe. And, like everything in life, it's an ongoing process. So give yourself time to make these changes. I believe change is most effective and long-lasting when it happens gradually and with awareness.

That said, these rules and principles are not to be taken as another giant *should* in your life. I will repeat this more than once: Let me give you permission up front *not* to have to be fabulous and gorgeous every time you step out the front door and not to have to buy the exactly perfect outfit every time you shop. If you've ever seen photos of movie stars off the red carpet and without makeup you know that perfection is a myth anyway.

As designer Isaac Mizrahi says, "The right amount of style is [about] knowing when not to have any." He explains that someone's best, effortlessly stylish "look" can happen when they tumble out of bed and throw on what they were wearing the previous day. I hope this book helps you get to the point where you can just throw on what you were wearing the previous day and still look and feel terrific.

Finally, if you peruse any number of fashion blogs or magazines these days you'll see images where many of the rules described here are flagrantly violated, often charmingly so. Keep in mind, though, that many of the fashion iconoclasts featured in these publications are either tall thin models, have a lot of drama, punch or swagger in their individual style type...or are under 30. So, absolutely go ahead and break the rules, any or all. Just make sure you are doing so intentionally, that your overall look makes the artistic statement you intend, and that what you're projecting is congruent with what you are on the inside. Or, as Dolly Parton says: "Know who you are and do it on purpose."

Here's to the Real You!

Your True Colors

The Case for Color

Being a visual person, I love color as much as I love fashion. (I'm guessing you do too, or you wouldn't have bought this book!) This can be a real problem. It's one thing to appreciate something visually appealing but quite another to adopt it for yourself. Yet we all do it.

Periodically, usually in the spring, fashion magazines scream, "Color Is *IN* This Year," which generally means that a particular palette of colors is what every sophisticated, fashion-forward shopper *must* wear. Stores are suddenly filled with dizzying racks of fuchsia, chartreuse and electric blue, mismatched patterns and color-block prints.

Once shoppers are saturated with the sensory onslaught and the fad has played out, it's a pretty good bet it'll be back to black next season. It's enough to give a shopper whiplash. Maybe it's the relentless, multitasking pace of Western culture that is behind this manic relationship with color—and with our black/tan/navy/gray comfort zone.

But in developing countries from Kenya to Brazil, from Thailand to Nicaragua, people adorn themselves from head to toe in color: bright, vibrant, sometimes brilliant colors. Yes, I realize those colors work beautifully on darker skin tones and reflect the specific weather conditions, geography, and culinary flavors of those countries. But it's not just in equatorial countries that the love of color is ubiquitous.

I had the good fortune to visit the Czech Republic shortly after the fall of the Berlin Wall. Away from the booming cosmopolitan atmosphere of Prague, many of the smaller cities still reflected the drab hopelessness of the Soviet era. I had fully expected to see all the women and teenagers dressed in either gray or black to match the bleak environment.

What I found instead was an explosion of color. Nearly everyone—boy and girl, woman and man—sported a chic, colorful winter coat, or at the very least, a bright, richly patterned scarf or hat. What this said to me was "in spite of my surroundings, in spite of the fact that my country has been trod on by every army marauding its way through Central Europe for centuries, I am still hopeful, creative, and alive."

I say, if they can do it, we can too. We must. Knowing and wearing our true colors is a gift we give to ourselves and to the world.

Your True Colors

When the pioneers of color analysis spoke of their ideal, they called it color *harmony* for a reason: It expresses the beauty, balance and order that exist in nature—and in you as an individual. It's all the more reason to look with a skeptical eye toward the latest fashions and fads, and to turn your awareness inward to your own color identity. The purpose of wearing the colors most flattering for you, besides the fact that you feel happy when you wear them, is that they make you appear healthy and enhance your natural coloring. Knowing and wearing your true colors is also very self-affirming.

By the time we reach adulthood, most of us have a general, if somewhat limited, idea of the colors that we can wear. But often that results in this lament: "Oh, I just can't wear red," or "greens make me look sickly." The fact is that *everyone* can wear reds, just as everyone can wear greens and blues. It is the specific shade, tint and undertone of a particular color that varies from person to person. I say *vive la différence*!

The recent popular standard for identifying someone's color palette has been to correlate their coloring with that of the four seasons: winter, spring, summer and fall. But considering the fact that there are more than three billion women in the world today the concept that we each fit into a pre-determined set of four seasonal color palettes is not very helpful and can be downright frustrating. I don't fault anyone for embracing this simple, elegant concept. In fact, we'll build on this very idea. Just keep in mind that you are a unique individual with a color palette all your own.

We'll start by going over some simple terminology of color theory. Then we'll help you set the foundation for your own palette by applying three principles: amount of saturation, contrast level, and undertone "temperature." With just those three principles you can pretty much determine if any color is in your palette. The four brief seasonal color charts that follow will provide a visual reference for the general range of colors that can work for you.

Once you get a good sense of your palette colors you may want to gather some reference material to bring with you when you shop. Some women do this by keeping a folder of clippings from magazines and catalogs with images that represent their palette colors. Or they collect fabric swatches in colors they know look good on them. (I don't recommend keeping pictures on your cell phone yet as color accuracy on digital devices still varies widely.) By placing a garment up against those images or swatches you can see if its color works with the rest of your wardrobe. At the conclusion of this chapter is a questionnaire that will to help you analyze the color of any garment you're not sure about. It's a good idea to keep a copy of it handy when you shop.

For those who want to take the entire process to a higher level you can seek the help of a professional color analyst who will do the work for you. There's nothing like having an expert pair of eyes to build or fine-tune your palette. (It goes without saying that if you have any degree of color-blindness, you must work with a professional.) When you do an Internet search for *individual color analysis* you'll find dozens of individuals and organizations providing this service. Some of these individuals are highly skilled and talented; some are graduates of color school diploma "factories." Be sure to look at the consultant's credentials, education and affiliations, speak with their former clients, and look at the colors they have selected for those clients. What you want is someone with artistic training and skill, a good eye, and an intuitive sense for color. You're making a big investment, not just in the initial cost of the analysis but in all the clothing you will buy based on the analyst's recommendations.

Whether you go it alone or hire a pro, you'll discover that building a wardrobe based on your color palette is a very personal process. It's as much art as it is science, and it takes time. But it's also extremely gratifying—and a lot of fun!

So let's start by going over some basic terms of color theory:

❖ *Saturation* refers to the depth or intensity of a color. Think about nail polish: a color that looks great in the bottle can be too pale if you use only one coat. To achieve the same color that you see in the bottle you have to apply multiple coats. That's what is meant by the level of saturation of a color.

❖ *Contrast* refers to the difference in saturation levels between two colors; we also use it here to describe the difference in saturation of skin tone, hair and eye colors.

❖ *Warmth* describes how much red or yellow is in a color.

❖ *Coolness* refers to how much blue is in a color.

❖ Bright implies a clear and unadulterated color—one that is not as intense as a more heavily layered one. You don't think of softer, whitened pastel colors or neutral colors as bright. You don't think of anything toned down with black or brown as being bright.

❖ *Tint* describes a color created by adding white to lessen the saturation of the original color. One example would be to create pink by adding white to red.

❖ Shade refers to a range of lightness to darkness in the same color family, e.g., coral, brick and burnt sienna are in the same general color family—warm rich reds—but each is a different shade.

With all this in mind, we'll examine three fundamental principles of individual color typing: 1) Contrast 2) Saturation and 3) Color undertone "temperature."

Contrast

First of all, examine your color markers: Hair, skin, and eye color. What you're looking to see is how much they contrast sharply, blend gently, or complement each other. This will determine how saturated the colors of your palette can be. For example, someone with very pale skin and extremely dark hair and eyes has a lot of contrast in their coloring. Someone with olive or honey skin tone, auburn or medium brown hair and hazel eyes has less contrast in their coloring. Someone with medium to light skin tone, soft brown hair and gray eyes has very little contrast in their coloring. Make note of how much contrast you see in your color markers.

Saturation

The greater the amount of contrast between your color markers, the greater will be the amount of saturation in your palette colors. When we describe the seasonal archetypes in this chapter (we'll also talk about seasonal combinations) you'll get a better idea of how saturated your palette colors can be. Always make this concept of *saturation* level a fundamental principle when determining whether any color is right for you.

Color Undertone Temperature

Finally, knowing where you fall in the color temperature range will give you the foundation for most of the colors in your palette. This is the first thing that every sales associate at a cosmetic counter looks for, although even they sometimes get it wrong. Basically, skin with blue undertones is considered cool and skin with yellow or red undertones is considered warm. This means that someone with cooler skin undertones will have reds, blues, greens and purples in their palettes that lean toward the blue range. Someone with warm undertones will have those colors in their palette that lean toward the red or yellow range.

Here are three ways to help you determine whether you will have predominantly cool or warm skin undertones. The other color markers that follow will help you add a layer of confirmation to your observation.

1) **Skin:** Undertones are very obvious on some of us but on others it's more subtle. Factors such as age, what you're wearing and even the lighting in a room can influence what you see.

   Nonetheless, we all fall somewhere within the range from extremely warm to extremely cool skin undertones. To analyze your skin look at yourself in natural light with as few environmental influences as possible, wearing a neutral-toned garment. Then look at skin that has been less exposed to the sun, such as the underside of your wrist or the crook of your elbow. The veins on that thinner skin will appear to be slightly green if your basic coloring is warm and bluer if your basic coloring is cool. (Yellow-toned skin over blue veins turns them greenish; blue-toned skin over blue veins just makes them look bluer.)

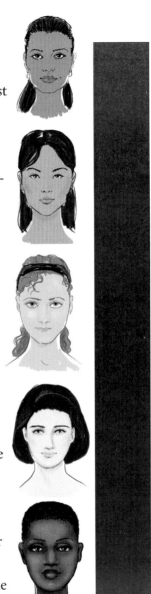

If that's not a clear indication, look at the inside of your lip or gums. Someone with cool undertones will have more blue/purple coloring, while those with warmer undertones might appear a little more orange/peach/yellow.

And if those aren't conclusive, here's an easy, and often accurate, way to determine your color undertone temperature. Simply compare yourself to a friend who has a markedly different undertone (*not* necessarily a different ethnicity) than your own. Sometimes that comparison is all you need. Again, make sure to compare the underside of your arms. (A tan will make anyone's skin tone look warmer.) Just keep in mind that there is a range of cool to warm skin tones. Some skintones are very warm and some are very cool but most of us fall between the two extremes, which explains why most of us bridge more than one seasonal color archetype.

In general, those with very pale, light ivory or extremely dark (blue/black) skin tones are considered in the cooler spectrum, meaning there will be a greater influence of blue and/or white throughout their palette. That pretty much describes the winter and summer archetypes.

Those with a pink-y flush on their skin will have an overall warmer palette, leaning more toward reds than yellows. Those with olive or dark skin with a peach-y flush are also considered warm but will have a greater influence of yellow than red throughout their palette. Those two pretty much describe the spring and fall archetypes respectively.

If you've looked at your skin tone and it seems sort of in-between—neither decisively warm or cool—these other color markers can help you determine your palette temperature.

2) **Eyes:** Gray, blue, and blue-violet eye colors are indicators of a cooler color palette. Brown, green, and hazel eyes are associated with warmer palettes. Very dark brown and black eyes usually indicate a cooler one, but will be influenced by a person's other color markers.

3) *Hair:* Next to your skin tone your hair provides the greatest volume of color to examine. But for many reasons, hair can be a tricky part of your color ecosystem. Our hair color changes throughout our lifetime, as does the texture. (My dad, born a towhead, grew up to have a thick head of curly black hair.) Then there's the fact is that more than 60 percent of us end up coloring our hair.

Take a close look at the variety of colors in your natural hair. If it's changed over time, or you've colored it for years, look at a picture of yourself before time, nature, or your colorist altered it. To get an idea of your basic hair color temperature find a swath of hair toward the back of your head or near the nape of your neck. That hair is the least exposed to the sun. If you have short hair, ask your hairdresser what the base color is.

Generally, very dark black hair, lighter brunette, ashy brown and naturally extremely pale blonde hair will indicate a cooler palette. Medium-to-dark brown, darker red and blonde hair, especially all those with natural highlights, will indicate an overall warm palette.

IN SUMMARY

The cool crowd:

- **Skin:** Very light or pale ivory or very dark with a bluish undertone.
- **Eyes:** Black, dark blue, very pale blue, gray, or violet.
- **Hair:** Jet-black, white-blonde, soft brunette, or ashy brown.

The hot club:

- **Skin:** Warm ivory, olive, ruddy, mahogany or reddish browns, peaches-and-cream, peachy-pink or yellow undertones.
- **Eyes:** Brown, bright blue, hazel or green.
- **Hair:** Yellowy or gold blonde, red, medium brown, mahogany.

Face Shape, the Non-color Determinant

This was something observed by Suzanne Caygill when she first began painting individual palettes for her clients. She noticed that certain color archetypes seemed to correlate with certain face shapes. Although her observation is something of an outlier in the field of color analysis, it can be the one factor that brings into focus a color palette that is complex or atypical. What Caygill found was that, generally, those whose faces were somewhat oval tended to have cooler palettes and those with some angularity or roundness had warmer ones. It's an intriguing concept and if your other color markers are inconclusive, it just might be the thing that helps you determine what your basic color temperature is.

Mixers

If there is a lot of striking contrast between your skin and your hair color (generally indicating a cooler palette) but your eyes are a warmish hazel color, (a warm color marker) your palette will combine both cool and warm colors, but only in the proportion that they're represented, or by the degree that a certain color marker really stands out. For example, if your eye color is a particularly striking feature of your coloring it may carry more weight when choosing your palette colors.

Building your Color Palette

Now that you have a basic understanding of the concepts of saturation, contrast and undertone temperature you can start building your unique palette.

The Eyes Have It

As just suggested, although our eyes are such a small part of our bodies, they have a significant impact on a color palette. In the film *Coco Before Chanel* there's a scene where a fabric salesman tries to convince the designer that she should buy a cut of pink chiffon rather than the black chiffon she has chosen. She replies: "No—black shows off the eyes." For her that was absolutely true. She had very striking color markers and her eyes were nearly coal black (and her iconic Little Black Dresses emphasized the fact). For those of us whose eyes are not black, the statement is something of a disservice. Yes, black creates a dark backdrop that makes you *want* to look at something lively—the eyes! But for some, wearing black near the face can actually dull the eyes unless you wear a lot of eye makeup.

Still, Coco was on to something. Wearing *your* eye colors definitely shows off your eyes. It also makes what you say more believable: the eyes are the windows of the soul, and wearing your eye colors invites people to look into that soul with trust. Your eye colors also make you feel calm when you wear them.

If you look carefully, you'll notice that just about every person has multiple colors in the iris of their eyes. Take a long, objective look at your own eyes and note all the colors you see. Any of these specific colors will be part of your palette. But you can also wear colors that are the combination of any of those colors or that fall between them.

For example, if your eyes are nearly black but have some burgundy (yes, some very dark eyes have beautiful dark red—or even gold!—flecks) you can likely wear a wide range of dark and saturated reds. If your irises are blue and contain a variety of tints of blue you can wear any of the blues or indigos that fall between the colors you see. Just be sure not to go paler or more saturated than your actual eye colors. If your eyes have brown, green or yellow flecks, you can wear any of the shades you see and/or that result from combining them.

Your Hair Colors

All the colors in your hair—natural highlights and all—will also be part of your palette. But wearing something that is exactly a hair color requires some caution. If your hair is black, that's a no-brainer. Go for it. But if your hair is a bright shade of red your outfit will really stand out; be sure you *really* want it to! And for those with hair that is a more subtle shade of brown, that brown will be a good neutral for you, but too much of it may just make you disappear. Definitely include your hair colors in your palette but recognize that they might work best for you as a neutral or an accent color rather than an overall one depending on your coloring.

Now that you have identified some of your unique colors based on your color markers let's move onto the concept of seasonal color harmony. This is the template for selecting the other colors in your palette.

Where the Seasonal Archetypes Come From

Color and style pioneers Grace Morton, Harriet McJimsey and Suzanne Caygill understood that we, as a part of nature, must necessarily reflect nature in our coloring. It was their keen observations that led them to associate an individual's color palette with the seasons of the year: winter, spring, summer, and fall. For descriptive purposes, we'll refer to them here as Striking Contrast, Lively Bright, Subtle Blended and Earthy Rich types.

Below are the descriptions of the four archetypal seasonal palettes. The color fans shown with them provide a small sampling of each season's colors and will give you a sense of the amount of contrast, the saturation level and the temperature undertone associated with each palette. In certain parts of the world and perhaps in certain parts of your own community there are gene pool clusters of these color archetypes. Think about your own ancestry as a starting point and you'll get a sense of where you may fit in the seasonal color categories. You'll start to see more clearly what you have inherited from your ancestors, and what variations you offer your descendants.

But remember this key point: Many of us, particularly in the West, don't fall under just one color archetype. We are often a combination of cultural and ethnic influences. And in fact, within every ethnicity there are some individuals who have warm color markers and some who have cool ones.

Also, just as the seasons transition gradually, so do the seasonal palettes. The colors in the early spring are very bright; in the later spring they're less intense. So not only will your coloring likely reflect more than one season, your most flattering colors within that season will vary based on your specific color markers. As you read through the seasonal archetype descriptions below, see which one or ones you resonate with most.

Striking Contrast (winter): Think primary, cool, and saturated colors. This coloring describes the winter season when we create colorful drama inside to contrast with the icy drama outside. These colors suggest the starkness, danger and beauty we associate with winter. Its intensely saturated hues are what designers call the jewel tones. A pure archetypal winter type will have skin tone and hair color in sharp distinction: very pale porcelain skin and very dark hair. Conversely, they may have a skin tone that is very dark, almost blue-black. (Occasionally you'll find a Striking Contrast type with extremely pale skin and white hair, but these types border on Bright coloring.) They are a study in extremes and contrasts and therefore can wear those colors that contrast or bounce off each other without being eclipsed by their intensity. In fact, if a pure winter type doesn't wear colors that are either bold (including stark black and bright white) or that contrast strongly, they can appear boring or seem to disappear.

Brilliant, clear colors on a Striking Contrast type are as luscious as they are harsh on someone with warmer or less saturated color markers.

* Their reds are clear and intense: shocking pink, scarlet, and crimson. Their pinks can glow like neon lights—in fact Bolds can wear many opaque neon colors.

* Their blues are deep and concentrated: sapphire, indigo, ultramarine, and bright turquoise.

* Their yellows vibrate like cadmium and canary.

* Their greens include rich emerald and chartreuse.

* Their purples are clear or intense like royal purple and saturated orchid.

* Their oranges are like bright tangelos.

* Their blacks are licorice, jet and onyx, and blue-black.

* Their whites vibrate like artic winter snow.

Sometimes an archetypal Striking Contrast type will have a distinctly longer oval face shape. Their eyes can be icy blue, jet-black or, as in the case of Liz Taylor, almost blue-violet. Their jewelry is cool and shiny, and diamonds are their best friend. In fact, they seem to shine like fiery diamonds, capturing your attention with their commanding presence.

Lively Bright (spring): Think of the playful colors of spring, the season of rejuvenation and regeneration. Spring is the season that takes us out of icy winter's contrast and into the emergence of the sun's warmth. When you think of spring colors, think *burgeoning* rather than stark. The spring season and the colors associated with it imply warmth and approachability. Like winter's colors, Lively Bright colors are also clear, but because they are less saturated they read more playful than dramatic. These colors are tinted lighter and often warmer than winter's more intense, cool ones. Think of the joyous purples of spring irises, refreshing yellows and oranges of daffodils, and the warm, glow-y quality of springtime sunlight. Think Easter eggs. Think *energy*!

✤   Their reds are warmer, less forceful than Striking Contrast but still clear and reflective: cherry red, bright pinks (like bubble gum!) and reddish fuchsias.

✤   Their blues are lighter turquoises, sky blue, cornflower, and robin's egg.

✤   Their yellows are cheerful like rich egg yolks and bright daffodils.

✤   Their purples include the range from violet to heliotrope.

✤   Their greens are apple and lime.

✤   Their oranges are poppy and...well, orange!

- ✤ They also include what designers consider the active, or sherbet colors: tangerine, lime, grape, and peach.

- ✤ Their whites are pure—not yellowed or grayed.

- ✤ Their blacks are clear, not mixed with brown, but less intense than something like onyx.

There is a youthful quality to a pure Lively Bright type, no matter what their age. Their hair and skin coloring pops with reflected light. Their skin has a pinky, flushed quality regardless of ethnicity. They may be redheads, blondes, or brunettes, but their natural hair color will likely consist of multiple shades and highlights of the base color. The strict archetypes often have green (not hazel) or bright blue eyes. Their faces tend toward roundness rather than angularity or elongation. If their face is not round in shape there is usually some round element such as cheeks, chin, forehead, or large round eyes. Multicolored gemstones or colored acrylic jewelry reflects their exuberant nature. Like the Striking Contrasts, Lively Brights also shine, but they cast their bubbly glow outward, illuminating the environment around them.

Subtle Blended (summer): Think soft, subtle, and cool—not just in coloring but in expression. Think of the shimmering sky at dawn and dusk or the easy calm of a carefree summer day. Summer's palette colors are those we associate with whitewashed beach cottages and comfy chairs upholstered in faded cabbage rose chintz. Think easy-going, laid-back. These types, although also on the cool spectrum, are the opposite of Striking's contrast. Their shine is more iridescent than neon. Theirs are the powdery or grayed colors suggesting subtlety, calm and restraint. Anything too saturated will overwhelm that subtlety.

✤ Their reds are gentle: rose, rose quartz, raspberry, salmon, and deeper fuchsias.

✤ Their blues are teal, French, slate, and cornflower.

✤ Their yellows are like pale corn silk, and banana.

✤ Their greens are cool like sage, celadon, and seafoam.

✤ Their purples are periwinkle, thistle, iris, and mauve.

✤ Their oranges are like pale tangerines.

✤ Their whites are ivory, blush, and can even include a pink-y seashell color.

✤ Their blacks are chalky, whitened-gray, and charcoal.

Those Subtle Blended types with dark hair and eyes can have light, somewhat contrasting skin tones. But that contrast will have less intensity than that of the Striking types. Their hair colors can range

from blonde to black, but will have a more washed quality. Their color markers seems to blend rather than pop. The eye color of these Subtle Blended types can range from soft or medium brown to pale green, pale blue or blue-gray, and the irises might have a characteristic darker color ring around them.

They do not command immediate attention and, consequently, people tend to pull closer to them in order to experience their quiet expressions more clearly. Subtle Blended types will never be in-your-face. Still, although they may appear quiet they often have a steady and determined character. There is a refined quality to their personalities that is reflected in what they wear: they're more likely to wear soft knitted materials than crisp ones, supple suede than leather. Like winters, their cool sisters, classic Subtle Blended types have face shapes that tend to be oval but not as elongated as pure winter types. They have an almost pearlescent quality and can wear mother of pearl or real pearls—pink, gray, white, multicolored—beautifully. Their soft presence draws you into their soothing world—without your even being aware it's even happening.

Earthy Rich (autumn): Think of the earthy quality of fall, the season of transformation and the abundance of the harvest. The bright oranges, crimsons, and golden leaves of autumn, the pumpkins, gourds, and nearly every shade of apples inform the palette of someone with Earthy Rich coloring. Think of minerals, spices, and earth tones. Think of brilliant orange sunsets. The intensity of autumn's deep warm colors hints at the drama to come in the winter. Even though autumn types exude a kind of maturity there's still something a little bit wild, sensuous and unpredictable about them, just like the weather in the autumn. Whereas Bright spring types reflect light outward, Earthy Rich ones keep the heat smoldering inside.

Their colors are unambiguous but complex. The warmth in their palette, as a characteristic of fall colors, leans more toward yellow than red. Their palettes are darker and have less clarity than Lively Bright colors, and are more likely to be toned down with black or brown instead of lightened with white.

* Their reds range from pomegranate to maroon, from brick to peach, from burnt sienna to coral.

* Their blues are beryl, teal, Persian, and Prussian.

* Their yellows are lush and rich like jonquil, gold, wheat, mustard, and amber.

* Their greens are earthy like asparagus, olive, and sage.

* Their oranges are pumpkin, ginger, and butterscotch.

* Their purples are mulberry, plum, and eggplant.

* Their whites are warm: cream, ivory, and palest beige.

* Their blacks are often tempered with yellow or brown and can appear more like a dark taupe or charcoal than black.

They have an earthy sensual quality, expressing the abundant richness of the season they reflect. Their skin tones can range from slightly warm ivory or olive to rich brown, often with peach, brick, or honeyed undertones. Their hair can run the gamut from auburn and copper to dark brunette or even dark blonde, but will likely have some warmer base tones and highlights. Pure Earthy Rich types have eyes that are most likely brown or hazel. Earthy as they are, they can wear ethnic jewelry that reflects earth colors and is made of stones or beads that have rich textures. The archetypal Earthy Rich faces often have some angularity—square, rectangle, or angled oval shapes. They have a warm, comforting presence that makes you want to settle at home in their world.

OK—so, there are the four archetypes. Repeat: *archetypes.*

If you are certain that you fall within only one seasonal color range, congratulations! Your shopping life will be very easy. (And you probably already know a lot of your best colors.) But again, for most of us, the idea that we each fit into just one of four color palettes is not very useful, and can be downright frustrating.

Filling in Your Palette

So, try this: Place your palm horizontally over the color fans shown for each season. Then turn your hand over so that your palm is facing up with the fan beneath it. (The difference between the color on your palm and the back of your hand will help you confirm whether the palette, or a particular color in it, works for you or not.) You'll likely find that one or two palettes speak to you more than the others.

Now place your hand vertically over each of the individual colors in the palettes. Do you find that there are some specific colors in another fan that work for your coloring too? Or are there even some colors in a third fan that you can also see yourself wearing? (It's very possible that you'll find some colors in two or three fans that work for you, but it would be highly unusual to find your coloring in all four-at least I've never seen anyone with colors in all four.) The more colors that work for you from a particular palette, the greater is the likelihood that this will be the dominant seasonal foundation of your own unique palette.

Always keep in mind the concept of contrast. You may find a color in another fan that almost works for you, but you may need it to be more or less saturated. The same goes for color temperature. A similar color that is close but too warm or too cool for your coloring will likely stand out like a sore thumb.

Just as you can combine your eye colors, you can also blend any of the primary colors that you know you can wear. For example, combining your specific reds and blues will create the right range of purples for you; combining your yellows and blues will create your best range of greens. Mixing those combined colors with any of your neutrals (black, dark brown, dark gray or charcoal) creates the subtle dark colors that can look terrific as outerwear or suiting materials.

How can you train your eye to see these mixed colors? Well of course, you could play with a watercolor paint set (I've tried it—I don't recommend it unless you're an artist—I'm not). Just pay attention to the undertone and saturation level of the colors you want to combine. Over time you'll start seeing the difference between, for example, a cool green (eucalyptus) and a warm one (olive). If you're unsure about a garment in one of the more complex or darker colors use the color questionnaire at the end of this chapter. It will make it pretty obvious whether the color works for you.

On the lightest end of your palette are your pastels. Everyone has some pastels. That's a good thing, because pastels make everyone appear fresh and bright. Your specific pastels will be the result of combining your lightest reds, (that includes red, pinks, fuchsia, coral, or peach, depending on your skin undertone) greens, blues or purples with a little of *your* version of white. Just make sure you don't go too pale for your coloring. The whole point is to look fresh and youthful, not washed out.

Using your specific color markers (skin, eyes, and hair), your skin undertone temperature, an understanding of the amount of contrast in your color markers, and the seasonal color fans you should now have a broad idea of your ideal colors and a good foundation for your unique palette.

Is This Color Me?

Below is a mental checklist to take with you when you shop. If you don't have your swatches or reference book with you, be sure to place any garment you are considering up to your face, preferably in natural light. (I've set off more than one store alarm walking a garment toward a window at the front of a store.)

When you hold a garment up to your face it should echo or complement your coloring rather than overshadow it. In fact, your eyes, your skin and your other features should pop if it's the right color.

Also, pay attention to the sheerness or opacity of a fabric. A sheer color on darker skin will read very differently than on lighter skin. [Note: Color analysts I've spoken with say that a summer tan makes no difference in one's basic color palette. However, I've found that those whose skin tones are in the warm range can wear more saturated versions of some of the colors in their palette or even brighter whites when they've spent some time in the sun.]

An additional thought: Just as with wearing a garment in your hair color, one that is exactly your skin tone can be very sexy and/or refined, depending on the fabric and the cut. But in some cases it can make you disappear. Just make sure it's right for the environment and circumstances in which it will be worn.

Color checklist:

- ✔ *Does my eye color fade against this color? Wrong color. Do my eyes look brighter? Right color.*
- ✔ *Does the color vibrate too strongly on its own against my skin tone? Wrong color. Does it complement or make my skin vibrate and come alive? Right color.*

✔ *Does my skin look washed-out, gray, or yellow against this color? Wrong color. Do I look healthier overall? Right color.*

✔ *Does the color highlight imperfections in my skin tone? Wrong color. Does my skin look smoother, more even-toned? Right color.*

✔ *Does the color fall somewhere in the range between two colors that I am certain I look good in? Right color. (Again: Make sure the color is not more saturated, paler, or of a different color temperature than one you know you can wear.)*

✔ *Do my friends say, "What a great dress, shirt, coat?" Be wary. But if they say, "You look great in that dress, shirt, coat," it's more likely a home run.*

✔ *Is the color something my best friend, mom, or boyfriend picked out for me because they love the color and/or look good in it themselves? Caution!*

✔ *Did I choose that color because my sweetheart's ex used to wear it? OK—if you have the ex's exact same coloring! (Even so, caution!)*

✔ *Do I say yes! immediately and then another yes! 10 minutes later? Buy it.*

One sanity tip: If that bridesmaid's dress or work or school uniform is in a color that just sucks on you—suck it up, wear flattering makeup...and your beautiful smile. That's how people will remember you.

Based on an actual bridesmaid dress seen recently...honestly.

Ask yourself: *Am I wearing my true colors?*

Working With Your Colors

2

By now you have a basic understanding about personal color typing and maybe you've even pulled together a fan or file of colors you know you look good in. But if your coloring is anything like mine (a combination of three different seasons) you're going to have to be more thoughtful when you shop than someone with fewer options. It just is what it is.

Whether you go the professional route or develop your own color book of swatches, take some time to live with your new colors for a while before making any drastic changes to your wardrobe. For most of us it takes time to let go of long-held beliefs about what colors we can wear and to embrace some we never thought we could.

So, if you've discovered a new color that works for you, how do you introduce it into your wardrobe? Start with something small. That will help you become familiar with what it looks and feels like to wear something so new and different. If you're not completely sure the color is right but you are very attracted to it, try it out as an accessory or a nail polish—something to play with for a while.

If it's a new color that you're certain works, I say go bold! That doesn't mean clownish or gaudy. It simply means you might want to consider opting for that very chic red, green or purple winter coat rather than basic black, navy or camel. Understand that wearing color makes you more visible. If you're timid about doing so (some people are afraid to stand out from the crowd) consider the possibility that you just might be giving everyone you encounter the one bright spot of their dull, colorless day!

What Colors Say

Having said that, it's useful to have a basic understanding of how different colors affect us—and those around us. Knowing the emotional and psychological impact of a color is an important part of choosing the right item for the right event and building a practical, wearable wardrobe.

Come here, honey. . .

"calm down now. . ."

Everything in nature has a kind of resonance—a vibration, if you will. So let's start by examining the vibrational qualities of each color and their effects on the psyche and emotions, both of the wearer and the viewer. We'll start with the primary colors, blue, red and yellow. Remember that everyone has some of all these colors in their unique palette with the exception, for some, of yellow.

Reds are romantic and stimulating. Red is the color of hemoglobin (literally life's blood) vitality, sensuality and danger. Wearing anything in the red family telegraphs these qualities, so make sure you really want to make a *red* statement when you wear it. For those who are not particularly romantic in their style type (which we discuss in Chapter 3) wearing the reds in their palette can make them appear more romantic. In fact, the less romantic quality in someone's personal style, the more they can get away with a lot of red without looking tart-y.

Reds that are tinted with white or light yellow—including pinks, salmon and peach—can make someone seem younger. Everyone has some lighter reds in their palette and these are useful when you want to appear more approachable and lighthearted. Reds tempered with black, like burgundy or maroon, create an impression of dignity and maturity, useful for when you want to be taken seriously. Corals and peaches—reds combined with yellow—express health and freshness. Reds combined with brown take on a rich, earthy quality and make someone appear grounded.

Blues are extremely versatile colors. They have the ability to express the full range of emotions from power and drama to calmness and serenity. [Note: Although people think of red as the most powerful color, my own color guru, John Kitchener, director of Personal Style Counselors, says that in fact blues—and some of the more saturated greens in your palette—are your true power colors. They express power in a more subtle manner.] Rich, saturated blues suggest authority and credibility. We wear these blues when we want to appear authoritative or exert influence. Your softer blues will make you appear relaxed and hopeful.

When toned down with black, creating the range of navy shades from indigo to what is called dark rinse in jeans, blues convey conservatism. Or, as with the jeans example, they become the great equalizer—a safe color for the masses. Blues washed with white are lively and crisp and suggest clarity of mind and spirit.

Yellows are some of the most intriguing and complex colors. They are the only ones that are limited for some people as they can turn some skin tones sallow. Depending where you live in the world, the color yellow has wildly diverse implications. It represents commerce in India, courage in Japan and mourning in Egypt. But in the West, we consider yellows to be jubilant. That's likely because they imply the liveliness and joy of the sun—the giver of life. They add spice, energy and warmth to anything they're worn with. In nature yellow flowers say optimism and good cheer. In their playful way yellows make a pretty bold color statement, especially in a workplace or social environment that favors a uniform of neutrals or dark colors.

Yellows can be youthful. They can also be versatile when combined with other colors. When toned down with black, they turn earthy, rich and grounding. When lightened with white, they're positively angelic and airborne! Yellow grabs our attention: When contrasted with black, as in street signs, it says, *Caution!* But in mineral form yellow becomes golden—warm, rich and rare.

Mixing Them Up

A lot happens when you combine the primary colors and tone them up or down with black and white.

Orange—the combination of red and yellow—reads *quirky* and *innovative*. It's a playful color that suggests joyfulness, creativity and compassion (think: Dalai Lama!) It's an outgoing, stimulating and healing color. Orange works really well for half-body garments, accents, and accessories, but too much of it can sometimes appear faddish.

Green says *security* and *endurance*. Bright yellow-greens are optimistic and suggest fertility, like the first leaves of spring grass. Greens lightened with white convey peace and calmness. Aqua—pale greenish blue—bestows peace on the viewer and in the environment. Turquoise—more blue than green—implies clarity and self-sufficiency. Teal implies trustworthiness. Anything in the teal range can help you make an impression or appear authoritative, but in a friendlier way than navy blue. Teal worn with your neutrals creates an elegant, crisp image. [Note: John Kitchener also describes teal blue as a universal color because it is the color of Earth from outer space, so we Earthlings all look good in it!]

Purple is comparatively rare in nature. Throughout history there was more difficulty producing purple dye for fabric. Because of its rarity and the fact that it carries the power of red and the elegance and authority of blue, purples are synonymous worldwide with royalty.

Lightened purples—lilacs, violets and lavenders—are ethereal and are associated with youthfulness in Western culture. One artist friend told me that everyone can wear orchid. (Of course, it depends on its saturation level and undertone.)

Homing in on your basic shades of reds, yellows, greens, and blues is an important start to understanding and wearing your true colors. But it's those in-between colors—the teals, plums, lilacs, tangerines—that take you to a whole other level of sophistication and distinctiveness. These shades express a range of qualities from lightheartedness to elegance and refinement. Buying a winter coat in a darker shade of one of the in-between colors in your palette can be just the thing to add real sophistication to your wardrobe.

The Neutral Zone

Paying attention to your specific neutrals and how they play on your coloring is extremely important because neutral pieces—suits, jackets, skirts and pants—will be the basics upon which to build your wardrobe. They are the go-tos that make the rest of your wardrobe sing. Hanging next to those playful multicolored dresses, blouses and sweaters they add balance and consistency and are repeatable and flexible.

So we'll start with the most basic neutrals: black and white. In the light spectrum, white is the combination of all colors, while black is the absence of all color. That fact sets the psychological tone for how we perceive black and white. But just as with primary colors the range of blacks and whites is vast.

Black: Not surprisingly, black is synonymous with danger, severity and, in many parts of the world, mourning. And yet, it has become so widely adopted by cultures around the world that it is now considered a safe—even sexy—neutral color. (Frankly, I credit Coco Chanel with that!)

So—must every woman wear black in order to appear chic? The French would certainly say *oui*! But, the answer is: it all depends. Once again, you'll have to let your color palette be your guide.

As we learned in the last chapter, cooler blacks, like licorice or jet-black, complement cooler skin tones whereas warmer blacks, like very dark taupe or charcoal, are more suitable for warm skin tones. Regardless of individual color temperature, some darker skin tones can get somewhat lost behind black, navy and darker browns. This is likely one reason why people in equatorial countries automatically gravitate to brighter, more saturated colors.

If you're one of those Striking Contrast types with paler skin tones, you can certainly continue to wear black in many forms: shiny, spangled and sequined, flat and dull, both as a wardrobe staple and a neutral.

Those with Subtle Blended coloring with cool undertones will have to be very careful about the kind of black fabric they choose. A garment in shiny or other highly reflective black can overwhelm their delicate complexions, particularly if their hair color is ashy or is sprinkled with gray. They'll look better in a flatter, less reflective black in quieter fabrics like linen or softer woven materials. Or they might just prefer to choose one of their darker gray shades as their darkest neutral.

Those with spring-like Lively Bright coloring can look great in black, particularly if they are willing to wear makeup that accentuates the brightness in their skin and eyes. They can go for either flat or even spangled black evening wear and also wear black in the duller fabrics. Their naturally brighter skin tones and often lighter eye colors provide a playful counterpoint to black's intrinsic heaviness.

Those with autumn's Earthy Rich coloring have to be a little more thoughtful in their selections of the shade of black they wear. As long as they have some peachiness in their skin tones they can wear some of the duller, flat blacks. And if their skin is a lighter honey or reddish mahogany shade, black can sometimes be downright sexy! However, on some Earthy Rich women with yellow undertones saturated black can make their skin look positively ashen. They'd likely do better in some of the lighter neutrals: ivory, cream and khaki. If they have an occasion for which black is required, they can simply keep their makeup-particularly for the cheeks and lips—more pronounced or if possible opt for something in the dark gray/beige or charcoal range.

White: We all tend to gravitate to white in the summer because it speaks to the warmth and light at that time of year. We gravitate to it in the winter as an antidote to the season's dreariness. Just about everyone can look lovely in the right shade of white. Make sure the white you wear brightens and enlivens your face. Winter white, a more ivory and warm color, can be very flattering on someone with warmer skin tones; it also works for those with very little contrast in their coloring. Crisp clear snow white can make someone with cool skin tones come alive but will make someone with a warmer skin tone appear gray.

Gray: Traditionally—and gray is a very traditional color—gray reads as sophisticated, conservative and crisp. A clean neutral, gray is particularly flattering for those with cooler skin tones. Gray mixed with yellow, green, or brown is more flattering on warmer skin tones.

Khaki, **warm beige** and **cream**: These are also chic, and tend to be more flattering to warmer skin tones than are clearer whites. Those with primarily winter or summer-like colors have a hard time with some tans and khakis as these can often dull them out. Someone with a warm skin undertone and predominant Earthy Rich coloring will have tans that have a touch of yellow in them. Those with spring-like Lively Bright coloring will have tans that have a little more red.

Navy: Brighter navy colors work best on those with Bright skin tones. Darker navy can look elegant both on winter and summer coloring. A grayed navy is one of the few darker colors that can be extremely flattering on the Subtle Blended types. Those with Earthy Rich coloring would do best opting for something in a more blackened dark blue range (think of Japanese indigo dyes).

All these neutral colors imply *professional* and intensify any color with which they're worn.

Brown: This color runs the gamut from yellow-y to reddish. You guess right if you figured that they look better on warmer skin tones. In general, this combination of black and yellow conveys warmth and earthiness and is not as widely used in business settings. That's most likely because people tend to associate cooler colors with objectivity and professionalism, two qualities you want in a business person. Now, if you're a landscape architect or in the environmental field, for example, you may, in fact, want to emphasize your more earthy credentials! But if your coloring is warm and you want to convey a sense of cool professionalism, you can opt for some of your darker blues, grays or dark taupes.

Note: Some wardrobe consultants suggest that every wardrobe have a camel-colored coat. But camel can be a tricky color for some people. I personally find it a little boring, unless the styling is impeccably chic. (Now that I've said this, I'm sure it will be all the rage next season. Just you watch.) Be sure to check it against your undertone and the other colors in your palette.

Combining Your Wardrobe Colors

When you're blending your colors, again, keep the concept of *contrast* in mind. If you're mostly a cool Striking Contrast winter-type you can go for greater contrast: more saturated colors worn together with other very saturated colors or extremely light colors with extremely dark ones, e.g. black with bright white. Combining only very light colors might wash out your striking coloring.

If you're mostly a Lively Bright spring type, you can also wear your brightest colors with each other. Just pay attention to their saturation value. Sometimes wearing only bright colors together might come off a little too cutesy, unless it's in a print. Brights have the advantage that they can also combine brighter colors with both light and dark ones.

Those with primarily Subtle Blended palettes and coloring generally do better going for less contrast overall. They can combine almost any of their colors together since most of the colors in their palettes will blend gently anyway. They can also combine any of their neutrals— dark or light—with their brightest colors as long as they keep in mind the concept of subtlety rather than strong contrast.

Earthy Rich types can combine their brightest and/or more saturated colors with their darkest ones or with their neutrals. They can also wear their lightest and darkest colors in prints as long as neither color washes them out. Combining their neutrals with a pop of their brighter colors can be a flattering combination for them.

Wearing similar colors, tone on tone or in some cases even a single color head-to-toe, (that last one is something shorter women can get away with easily) is a very elegant look and can make you appear longer and leaner. It's generally works for just about everyone, unless it's in a color like bubblegum pink or chartreuse. Also, wearing two different shades of the same color with just a hint or accent of a contrasting or opposite color begins to take you in the direction of the divine Japanese aesthetic called *shibui*. Shibui describes an unforced look that suggests art, simplicity, quietude and modesty. But it also includes something— often a visual representation of something in nature—that breaks it up to avoid the sense of too much perfection. That additional unexpected element more closely mimics nature and real life.

Monochromes and tone-on-tone layering elongate the body; contrasting colors and color block prints shorten and break it up. It's just that simple.

As we mentioned earlier, although many of you may have a combination of some cool and some warm coloring (e.g., warm skin tone and cool eye colors) they are rarely represented in equal amounts. How do you deal with that? Judiciously.

You can certainly pair warm and cool colors. Just don't wear equal amounts of them, especially near your face. If you're a predominantly strikingly colored winter type but find that you can also wear some colors in the autumn palette, you'll appear more lively by favoring Striking colors near your face. For example, if your eyes are warm (lighter brown or hazel) wearing just a touch of one of your warm colors near your face—possibly in a print with your neutrals—can bring out your eyes. Wearing too much of it can make you look dull or appear out of harmony with the rest of your coloring and clothing.

Someone with very strong yellow undertones in their skin but with jet-black hair may have a palette that is predominantly Earthy Rich due to their skin undertone. But because of the depth of their hair color they will be able to wear more saturated shades of their brightest colors than most women with fall-type coloring. They will also be able to wear greater contrast in their colors.

Just think of the predominant seasonal influence in your coloring as the basis of your wardrobe, particularly for the colors you wear near your face, and then use your lesser seasonal influences as accents. And *always* keep the elements of contrast, saturation and undertone temperature in mind.

Neutrals with Colors

If you want to play around with neutrals and color, here are some fun ideas to try. For those with cooler palettes (winter and summer types) consider combining one of your cooler neutrals such as navy, gray, or black with one of the more saturated cool colors in your palette, e.g., royal or cobalt blue, lilac or a saturated fuchsia. It's a lovely way to display the range of your color harmony. For warmer palettes, try combining your warmer neutrals such as khakis, tans, and browns with some of the warmer and brighter colors in your palette like salmon, peach, aqua, or teal.

But for those who really want to create a true color imprint, here's a way to think about neutrals that can transform your wardrobe from uniform to something very sophisticated. Start with a classic, maybe an outerwear piece or suit, in one of your darker or more saturated neutrals, for example, burgundy or port, olive or forest green, eggplant or plum. Try pairing that with a blouse, dress, pant, or accessory in one of your brighter or more energetic colors such as turquoises, fern, or even lime greens, or possibly something in your orange range. It's a fun exercise well worth playing around with. You may come up with a combination of colors that you would never have even dreamed of but that is particularly lovely on you. (Don't always trust your memory on these combinations. Keep your smart phone handy and take a photo of yourself in the outfit if it works.) Be brave, have fun with your colors, and always make sure you are enhanced by them and not overshadowed by them.

Some Shopping (Hard) Facts of Life

Just so you know I'm not a Pollyanna about shopping for your more
unique colors. I clearly understand that finding them is not a slam
dunk. Also, some palettes are more unusual than others (my hand is
raised) and some people's colors are harder to find on the racks. (Ditto.)
For those with Subtle Blended summer coloring, shopping in the fall
often is a challenge. Likewise, for those of us with predominantly fall-
like Earthy Rich coloring finding our colors in summer-weight fabrics
is nearly impossible.

One more pet peeve: Some catalogs may have an item in your ideal
color but only carry it in men's sizes. Happens to me all the time. You
can always order the closest size in the men's version, but it will likely
be pretty shapeless. [By the way, at the end of this book is a list of the
most popular catalogs and clothing chains with a description of the
primary color palette, style type and sizes they consistently offer.]

Rather than seeing these limitations as a curse, think of them as a
blessing: having fewer choices translates into less complication in your
life. Whenever I lament the fact that I can't wear a certain popular
set of colors I remind myself of a line from a Joni Mitchell song about
how having too many choices can make you crazy. Having a more
limited wardrobe of things that are perfect for you is less expensive,
less confusing and more liberating than restocking an entire closet
every year.

In all fairness the fact is that, regardless of our individual color typing,
we do tend to be attracted to the colors associated with the seasons
which is why we crave brighter spring colors in the spring. As we come
out of the rigors of winter we *want* to embrace that springtime energy.
(I'm ignoring the "I-wear-all-black-all-the-time" folks, which describes
nearly everyone I saw at the theater the other night.) Psychologically,
brighter colors simply are more eye-catching to a casual shopper. So,

except for those anomalous years when you'll see pink blush in the fall and dark khaki in the spring, you're obviously going to find the colors associated with each season at the beginning of that season. The good news is that everyone has some brighter, clearer colors in their palette. Just make sure the ones you choose work for you, using the color questionnaire as your guide.

Here's another important point to keep in mind—something we'll clarify in the next chapter on style. There's a tendency for designers to confuse color archetypes with style archetypes. What that means is that they dress someone with winter-type coloring in more dramatically cut and styled clothing. They put someone with spring-type coloring in clothes with a more youthful style. Those summer color types are often stuck with very classical pieces. And autumn colored types often end up in denser fabrics, often with an outdoorsy or casual look. So be alert! Yes, there are some natural affinities between certain seasonal colors and certain style types. But that's not always the case for every individual.

So, with all that in mind, those seasons when you do find your colors, particularly those more unusual ones, *buy, buy, buy*! It's even a good idea to buy multiples in classic pieces like turtlenecks, cardigans or tees. If your colors are popular this year, you can bet that next year the same manufacturer will be showing them in a slightly different shade— one that's not yours—or not at all.

Finally, you might find a garment you absolutely love, but that is not exactly your color. If it's just a little off but looks fabulous on you just buy it. Or, if you want to be obsessive about it, as I tend to be about color, there's always the option of dyeing it. I've been known to take a favorite garment that is not quite the right color and dye it until it's in my ideal color range. (Of course we're talking about something simple like a cotton t-shirt or blouse, not a wool suit or cashmere sweater!) That way you will have a new garment you can wear for years with delight. If you go this route, be sure to research the fabric to determine whether it has any coating on it or if it can take additional color. Rit Dye has some great charts that describe how to dye different fabrics and tells you which colors to combine to get the one you want: ritdye.com

Color and Aging

The question of color and aging has come up frequently in my research. My opinion is that wearing color becomes even more important as we age in order to stay visible in a culture that idolizes youth. If you're one of those more mature and very artsy types who continues to boldly embrace the avant-garde in both color and style, I say go for it!

But for the rest of us, choosing the right colors becomes even more important and often more challenging as we age. This is because although our basic palette does not change, our coloring does tend to fade over time. Our skin does not reflect as much light as it did in our youth. (There are exceptions, of course. Until the day she passed away at 92, my pure Lively Bright friend Marguerite Lemmon had bright pink cheeks and wore her brightest colors easily.)

Aging Skin and Your Palette

For many women, wearing the less saturated versions of their brightest colors tends to be more flattering to an older face.

Wearing something in one of your lighter reds (which, depending on your palette could mean pinks, fuchsias, peaches or corals) can add a healthy reflected glow to the face. Wearing your eye colors is also flattering, as these draw attention to the part of the face that expresses your inner light.

If your skin tone has changed, certain colors can help balance out your coloring. The process works similarly to how makeup artists use warm, cool, or neutral makeup concealers to correct skin tone imbalances. The key lies in adding the color opposite to the one that is in excess. Those who have sun-damaged skin or age spots tend to look good in the whites in their palette. (Light khakis might also work for some.) These colors throw light on the face, add some brightness, and draw the eye away from dark spots—and toward the eyes.

Those whose skin has gone a pale or ashy gray benefit from the lightest reds in their palette: Pastel pinks, roses, or peach cast a lovely glow on cool or dull skin. Those who have turned ruddy can cool down that heat by wearing some of their cooler shades of blue and purple. And for those with sallow-looking skin, wearing their warmest reddish blues (like plum) or bluish reds (like fuchsia), can balance out yellow tones and add some vitality to the skin. Cooler blues might create too much contrast that will exaggerate excess yellowness.

Now, none of this means that you have to forgo bright colors and colorful patterns as you age. In fact, I hope you never do! It simply means that if you have an article of clothing that is on the brightest end of your palette you may want to check it carefully in natural light to make sure it isn't making you look pale or emphasizing some imbalance in your skin. Keep the color checklist from Chapter 1 handy. One more point: An article of clothing may have faded in the wash making its color less flattering on you than it had been originally. It's a good idea to recheck the color of old favorites against your skin tone periodically.

We talked about the importance of neutrals as an elegant and uncomplicated staple for any wardrobe. This becomes even truer as we age. I know some older women who have developed an entire wardrobe of either white or black! But even for those who have no intention of going to that extreme, it's a lot easier to add a little spice or sexiness to a classic neutral garment by pairing it with a beautiful blouse, sweater or sparkly top, or great piece of outerwear, than it is to take something in a wild pattern designed for a younger demographic and suddenly make it appear refined and age-appropriate. But remember, neutrals can be just the lightest and darkest versions of your basic palette. They don't have to be white, tan, gray and black.

Many stylists say that to look chic as you age, you must wear black—lots of it. Others say it pales you out. Again, only those women with a very high percentage of Striking Contrast or Bright coloring can continue to look great in black, particularly if their hair has turned white or salt-and-pepper. Again, it's all about undertone. Someone with cooler overall coloring and strongly contrasting color markers can easily wear black. Those with warmer or in-between skin tones just have to be careful about the kind of black they wear, and may instead want to opt for another neutral altogether.

Makeup and Aging

If you just love one of your old wardrobe pieces in one of your more saturated colors or colorful patterns but it suddenly seems a little overwhelming now, a little bit of the right makeup can make it wearable again. Now, a lot of older women give up on wearing makeup, figuring that it no longer matters how they look. (We Natural style types in particular find it such a bother sometimes.) At a certain point you just want to let it all hang out and just *be.* But the reality is that we are judged by the first impression we make. Letting age spots or imperfections just be is, of course, a healthy psychological attitude. But when you want to present yourself in the most flattering manner, the fewer distractions on your face the easier it is for others to experience your inner essence. (I'm not going to tell those with drooping lip rings to give them up-that's your call. I'm talking about skin.) Having clear, more luminous skin will allow the first impression you make to be your inner glow rather than your advancing years.

If you have worshipped the sun (as I have) and now see those age spots emerging (as I do) using a concealer and a dash of blush to balance out your skin tone will keep the eyes on your eyes and not your spots. Secondly, aging lips are increasingly colorless or dull. Giving yourself a little lip color can instantly transform your face from blah to bright. On some women, darker lip colors can be aging, so you might want to try your most flattering lighter reds, pinks, and corals. They will make you appear more vital. The rest is up to you. Personally, I love to see subtle eye makeup on older women. It shows they want to express with their eyes.

But in all these efforts I strongly encourage opting for the safest cosmetics out there—the ones with the fewest and least harmful chemical additives. It takes a little searching to find them, but they are becoming more plentiful and popular, and are well worth the effort. [On my website blog I'll be updating links to many of these periodically.]

Aging and Hair Color

In her kindness, Mother Nature softens our hair color as we age. The effect is a kind of halo that calls less attention to the wrinkles and aging skin that is no longer as elastic or full as it was. Some of the more dramatic or earthy types will gladly celebrate every line and earned wrinkle with panache and pride. I say bravo! But for those of us who choose to color our hair it's very important to find a colorist who clearly understands the concept of skin undertone and overall coloring. Covering or coloring graying hair is a complex calculation, particularly as the texture and the thickness of your hair changes over time.

As with an accessory that pops, you can certainly make a fashion statement by dying your hair a mono color. How well you carry it off will depend upon your coloring, personal style and, of course, your age.

Those with black or very dark brown hair well know the high-maintenance requirements of white roots. If your skin tone can handle keeping your color dark, do it. Diana Vreeland made dyed black hair her signature throughout her life and always looked stunning. Some of those lucky Striking Contrast types whose coloring is stark to begin with can look terrific when they let their hair go completely white. Bright white hair is intrinsically contrasting to anything worn with it. For those with salt-and-pepper hair letting it go all white, or selectively keeping swaths of gray or white, can be very sexy. (My gorgeous 60-something friend Anna who previously had jet-black hair let it turn completely white, showing off her luminous, bright blue eyes.)

Subtle/Soft coloring, cool in nature, also tends to gray beautifully. Anne Kreamer's wonderful book *Going Gray* chronicles a web dating experiment in which she posted one photo of herself with dyed hair and the other with her natural gray streaks. Guess what! Her gray hair look got more hits!

Blondes and redheads can go lighter than their original color as long as they stay within the same range of their basic undertone and highlight color: gold, copper or red. They just need to pay careful attention to how the color plays on their skin.

Many colorists I've spoken with usually encourage older women with graying brown hair to add a few highlights and/or lowlights to their color. For these women, their natural hair is rarely one color anyway. Subtle highlights, and especially lowlights, can bring softness to a face and lend credibility to dyed hair that is graying. They will also allow the gray hair to blend in almost invisibly as it grows out. For those who don't intend to color their graying brown hair, the silvery color that brown hair tends to turn with age can be particularly lovely and brightening to a face. It can also make some of your wardrobe colors "pop."

There is a tendency for those whose hair was originally dark and is now going gray to switch to something in the red range or with a good amount of red undertones. (The Baby Boom demographic demonstrates this: Sales of red hair dye have skyrocketed in the past few years.) Red can be a tricky hair color to work with on anyone but particularly on someone with very dark hair that is going gray. If your coloring is Striking Contrast or Subtle Blended a bright red can look fun and exciting, but it's a look that works only on someone with a pretty dramatic personal style. If your hair was black or very dark brown and you switch to a lighter warm red you may find your skin looking a little yellow or washed out. Also, you may suddenly find your wardrobe colors aren't as flattering as they once were.

Always let your skin tone be your, and your colorist's, guide about the shade of red you choose. You may even want to bring your color swatches with you to the salon to give your colorist more information about what color would best work for you.

Ask yourself: *Do the colors of my clothing and accessories—and hair— work together to represent and enhance the real me?*

An Important Note for Everyone

Since we're talking about hair color and make-up I want to close this chapter with another important health note. Questions about the environmental and personal safety of beauty care products are of increasing concern. It's a concern I share and encourage you to do as well. One periodic hair coloring, one hand cream, one eye shadow or lipstick may not cause noticeable or significant damage. It's the process of piling on multiple chemical additives in skin care products and heavy metals in cosmetics and dyes that over time get absorbed through the skin and can wreak havoc with the endocrine, lymphatic, and other systems in the body. I personally look at every skin care and hair product label carefully and try to buy those with only the most natural ingredients.

It's worth your time to do a little investigating into what you're putting on your face, your skin, and your head and what long-term impact these products might have on your health. The Environmental Working Group (ewg.org/skindeep/) has a fabulous website that indicates the carcinogenic potential for many beauty products based on their ingredients. Skin care maven Marta Wohrle's Truth in Aging site (truthinaging.com) has an encyclopedic reference section listing hundreds of common ingredients in beauty products, their function and their effect. She also includes links to research on many controversial ones. And then there's the Campaign for Safe Cosmetics (safecosmetics.org) for the latest news and research on cosmetics. Let's keep up the pressure on manufacturers to develop beauty products that are nontoxic both for us and our environment.

Your Unique Style

3

The subject of personal style seems as though it should be pretty straightforward. After all, it's just a matter of knowing what you look like and what you like to wear. But in fact, it's a highly charged topic. For one thing, many people don't want to be pegged as a single type; they like variety and change. That's what being fashion-forward is about, right? For others, what they wear is a deliberate artistic statement that has nothing to do with what they look like. And for many, the whole idea of evaluating oneself—features, body type, and personality—brings up a lot of self-esteem issues.

Just about everyone, especially in their teens, likes to try on different fashion styles before they find their own. Those who never do run the risk of remaining fashion victims year after year. They become like walking advertisements for someone else—a designer, a pop star, etc. When we don't understand our individual style we can be greatly influenced by the dictates of family, popular culture, and a desire to fit in. But individual style isn't something to be adopted; it's something to be revealed.

With that in mind, I want to invite you to consider the concept of individual style in the same spirit that we examined individual coloring. Think of it as an exploration into the basic principles of harmony that, rather than narrowing your options, offers you more or better ones. It's another step toward unfolding all the facets of your unique self to share with the world. Just as with coloring, consider this information about style as a series of guidelines to help you fine-tune your wardrobe, and not an inflexible set of rules.

One of the greatest rewards of understanding your personal style is authenticity. Living an authentic life is living a healthy life. In that vein, here are a few quotes to consider from some of my favorite philosophers and aesthetes.

> Some other life isn't necessarily the one for you.
> –KARL LAGERFELD

> If you're constantly living someone else's life, who is living yours?
> –BYRON KATIE

> The dharma of another brings danger.
> –BHAGAVAD-GITA

I included that last one because I think it's the most apt, but it requires a word of explanation. The Sanskrit word *dharma* can be defined as the principle or law that creates order and harmony in the universe, and in our lives. If you're spending a lot of time and energy trying to manufacture an image that's not yours, you're probably violating one of those universal laws that keep everything humming along. Not to mention creating a lot of inner stress. (Stress, as we all well know, leads to all kinds of problems.) So let's make life a little less stressful by helping you to understand and to learn to love *your* unique style.

Just as with color, one's style is fairly consistent throughout a lifetime, but changing circumstances and environments as well as the process of aging require us to be flexible in how we express that style. A 60-year-old woman may neither wear the same hemlines nor expose cleavage as readily as she might have at 30, but the ideal fabric textures, silhouettes, and types of accessories that best reflect who she is will not change much, if at all. It's true that body shape and bone structure can vary with dramatic weight changes. But if we understand the fundamentals of our style type, those changes may simply require a trip to the tailor rather than an overhaul at the mall.

The Elements of Style

You've probably seen the terms *classical*, *relaxed*, *bohemian*, and *elegant* used to describe different style types. This can be perplexing if you see yourself sometimes as elegant and other times as relaxed—or bohemian—or classic. Just as our coloring can represent several color harmonies, our features, body shape, and personality often reflects more than one style type. It's a rare person who is 100 percent buttoned-down and tailored or who can easily get away with purple spiked hair and full-body tattoos.

Looking at yourself subjectively—your personality and inner self— gives you an overview of your style type(s). These internal qualities can have a lot of influence on even the most definitive physical features. Then, by analyzing your features objectively e.g., bone structure, features, height, you can fill in some details about how your personal style can be expressed through what you wear. The entire process can be a quick review, confirming what you already know about yourself, or an educational project over a longer term.

Here are three subjective exercises to help you get a sense of your overall style. You can do any or all of them but each one adds a layer of confirmation. Following these are a series of charts that cover the more objective physical features.

Exercise One: This one might be a challenge but it can be very informative! Ask 10 of your closest or most trustworthy friends, family members, or coworkers to give you their one-word impression of your personality or overall style type. You might hear things like trustworthy, wild, refined, nurturing, playful, laid-back, dramatic, mischievous, energetic, fun-loving, sexy, reliable, fearless, etc. You might learn things about yourself you never knew—or wanted to know! Regardless, these snapshots will start to paint a picture. True, someone may come up with something completely out of character.

But if eight or nine say something similar about your style, that's pretty reliable.

For example, if your friends know you to be steady or reliable, it's not likely you live on the wild side. How does that translate to your wardrobe? You probably gravitate to and look great in more traditional, classic, or preppy styles. If you're considered laid-back or easygoing you may lean toward looser fitting, comfortable fabrics, yummy knits, and comfortable shoes. Dramatic or fearless? Your closet isn't likely to be filled with timid colors or delicate chiffons. You get the idea.

Because people are a combination of types, consider what the multiple adjectives you hear about your personal style imply collectively. If you're naughty (mischievous) but nice (steady) your personal style might include classic styles with a little toughness or sexiness; a pencil skirt, for example, with a sheer blouse and edgy shoes.

Exercise Two: Open your closet door. Pick out the things you love, that make you feel most authentically you when you wear them or that earn you consistent compliments. Apply the terms you've now learned about yourself (or, if you didn't try the previous exercise, come up with some self-descriptive words of your own) and see if those same terms accurately describe your favorite clothes. If they do, you really know yourself. If they don't, try this next exercise.

Exercise Three: This one takes some time but can be extremely valuable and accurate for the long run. And it's fun! What you're going to be creating is similar to what designers refer to as a vision or mood board—a collection of the colors, styles, and textures that speak to you on a deep level. (These can include the photos and color swatches you gathered to make up your color palette or they can be an entirely new set of images.) You can do this either on a large piece of inexpensive poster board or set up a Pinterest page. Over time, as you thumb through magazines, catalogs, or websites, clip out—or click on—the outfits or accessories that you think would be flattering on you. You can also select images of someone who resembles you in coloring or face shape, or who expresses how you perceive your personality, etc. Now, paste, tape, or post these images to your board or page in any form you like. As you add more images some patterns will begin to emerge. You'll find that if something is off, it will immediately stick out like a sore thumb.

After you've collected a fair number of these images, step back and look at the big picture. Ask yourself, what do these images have in common? Do they share a particular silhouette? Color palette? A similar scale, fabric texture, or pattern style? Cut or drape? What adjectives would you use to describe these pictures? Do those terms say the same things about you that you learned from the first two exercises?

It's a good idea to revisit your mood board every few seasons or even to make up a new one periodically. You'll be surprised to see how quickly fads and fashions change. Something that seemed new and fresh even a year ago can suddenly start to look dated. You'll also start to see your version of the classics emerge on that board: pieces that you tend to gravitate to regardless of season or fashion.

Now that you have a feeling for your general style facets you're ready for our style archetype charts. These charts delineate specifics about facial features, bone structure, etc. Before we start, let's look at where these style archetypes came from.

The Yin and Yang of It All

Asian influences on architecture, art, and fashion design flourished in the early 20th century and gave us a key insight into the nature of personal style. Inspired by Eastern philosophy, Belle Northrup, a professor of clothing design at Columbia Teachers College in the 1920s, first suggested that the Tao concepts of yin and yang were apt terms to describe an individual's style and personality.

Today these terms have become commonplace, but the way we understand them is somewhat limited. We tend to think of yin and yang as opposite values in life. In fact, they are simply two sides of the same coin. They reflect the coexistence of all elements and qualities in nature: sunlight and shade, dynamism and passivity, heaven and earth. Belle Northrup suggested that each person's features, coloring, and personality reflect yin and yang in varying proportions.

Grace Morton, fashion and textile professor at the University of Nebraska, took the concept a step further, identifying specific features and personality traits with the yin quality and others with yang.

Finally, following Morton's lead, Harriet McJimsey of Iowa State University developed a detailed chart of six individual style archetypes, ranked from most yang to most yin. She called these archetypes Dramatic, Athletic, Gamine, Classic, Romantic, and Ingenue. As broad and detailed as these archetypes were, they excluded those fragile beings among us who exist at a farthest yin end of the spectrum. My mentor, John Kitchener, felt that descriptions of the Ingenue archetype didn't do justice to their uniquely delicate features. After years of observation he outlined a new archetype, Angelic. It balanced out the most yang—Dramatic— and its addition places the Classic type squarely in the middle of the other six creating a total of seven archetypes. (We'll learn later why the Classic archetype is important to all of us, regardless of individual style and age.)

What I find so fascinating about Northrup, Morton, and McJimsey is that they recognized and celebrated the entire range of types of beauty long before popular culture homogenized and limited what is considered beautiful today. They were some of the first true feminists and I find it delightful that they lived in the world of fashion.

Based on my own observation and study I have expanded some of McJimsey's descriptions within these archetypes to include more ethnically diverse elements that bring the charts current, and am using the Personal Style Counselors category names. Once you learn where you fall within these style categories, you will most likely discover that you have elements of both yin and yang in your bone structure, coloring, and personality.

We don't need to think of these types as completely static throughout our lifetime. Both Morton and McJimsey explained that someone's style type is not fully formed until they reach maturity. By its very nature, youthfulness—or as McJimsey termed it, Ingenue—is synonymous with the young. Almost everyone has a large amount of the Youthful style facets in their youth. Until we lose some of our baby fat and grow into our skin, we can't really know what the structure of our face and body will be.

Maturity is a yang quality, and that yang gradually becomes expressed in both our features and behavior. Even the roundest face tends to square off somewhat with the effects of gravity and time. As we move into old age, those more yin qualities show up again. Our hair becomes paler in color and our skin and bodies become softer and less defined. Given the dynamic process of yin and yang throughout our lifetime, it's a good idea to reexamine some of our old wardrobe favorites periodically, even classic pieces. But always keep in mind that in spite of the changes you might undergo, your basic style will not change dramatically.

The categories in these charts cover just about any style type—or combination of style types—listed in popular magazines and websites. We'll go over some of those combinations following the charts. When reading an individual chart, just think of each category description of features, coloring, and aspects of personality simply as adjectives and modifiers (descriptive possibilities) of the noun—you! That will make them read less like hard-and-fast rules. It will also make it easier for you to see yourself in multiple style archetypes.

You'll see that there are several examples included for each category or physical feature. Make a check mark in the box next to *any* category that includes even a single example that accurately describes one of your features or personality traits. You may find similar descriptions of coloring, facial features, etc. in more than one chart. Check off all that pertain to you. Some archetypes have a natural affinity with each other—which we'll discuss later—and you will be reinforcing that connection.

The categories describing hair texture and style can be tricky. Many of us play around a lot with our hair texture, shape, and color. Those changes themselves can say a lot about one's style. For your purposes, consider how your hair looked *before* coloring, curling, or straightening, and before the influences of hormonal changes and sun damage. Then, also check any of the categories that describe the way you wear your hair now.

The categories of Expression, Environment, and Behavior can help give a general feeling for what makes each style type tick. You may find that they tie in with the terms you and your friends came up with to describe your style.

Plastic surgery is another topic that we'll discuss later in this chapter. For now, just go with what you see in the mirror.

When you're done, add up all your checkmarks for each style archetype. Your totals indicate how much each style archetype is reflected in your features, etc. The larger the number, the more you match that archetype. Then, read the archetype descriptions that follow to see if they match what you already know about yourself. After the descriptions we'll explain how they cover everything from *bohemian* to *chic* to *edgy*.

DRAMATIC		
OVERALL		**CHECK BOX**
Height	Tall: above 5'7"	
Body Shape/Build	Large boned; long legged; angular (rectangular body, shoulders waist and hips similar sized);	
Posture/Stance	Stands fashion-model straight; carries weight back on the heels; chin slightly elevated	
HEAD FEATURES		
Facial Structure	Long oval; elevated cheek bones; chiseled (flat plains on cheeks)	
Eyes	Angled or slanted upward; deep or close set; heavy lids; direct gaze	
Eyebrows	Sharply defined; angular	
Nose	Straight; long; pointed; convex; flared nostrils	
Mouth	Wide; lips are very thin or very heavy; flat; curved shape; lips held firmly	
Hairstyle	Severe style: clean, angular cut; center part; pulled back; large Afro; exaggerated widow's peak	
COLORING		
Overall	Extreme definition and contrast	
Hair	Black; dark auburn; dark brown; with age, stark white or white streak	
Skin	Blue-black; very dark brown; olive; cream	
Eyes	Black; Brown	
MANNER		
Behavior	Restrained power and dynamism; exciting	
Manner	Formal; dignified; reserved; sophisticated; haughty; panache	
Voice	Resonant; husky; low; emphatic; deliberate; good voice for radio or theater	
Walk/Gestures	Decisive/energetic or slow and purposeful	
Age Appearance	Appears mature at any age	
Environment	Their home is their showplace	
Dominant Expression	Danger can be interesting; boredom is death	

NATURAL		
OVERALL		**CHECK BOX**
Height	Above average: 5'5"–5'7"	
Body Shape/Build	Sturdy, muscular or athletic; broader square shoulders; more toned than fleshy	
Posture/Stance	Relaxed and casual or vigorous and alert; weight well-balanced on feet;	
HEAD FEATURES		
Facial Structure	Long; rectangular, square or softened square; broad; square or angular jaw; wide forehead	
Eyes	Average size for face; friendly, warm and approachable	
Eyebrows	Straight; natural; heavy or dark	
Nose	Strong shape; wide or heavy; long, angled or blunted angle	
Mouth	Wide; naturally smiling expression; average sized or full lips	
Hairstyle	Casual and natural; unfussy; large waves or worn very short; wiry; dreadlocks; medium sized Afro	
COLORING		
Overall	Natural and outdoorsy	
Hair	Dark; medium brown or auburn, can be red; with age turns salt and peppery or gray; more thick than fine	
Skin	Freckled; tanned; natural-looking; ivory; mahogany	
Eyes	Brown, Dark Brown; Hazel	
MANNER		
Behavior	Unaffected warmth	
Manner	Free; easy; frank; open; friendly; welcoming	
Voice	Strong; clear; natural, low pitched	
Walk/Gestures	Easy; relaxed and natural; long strides; nothing "tight" in their gait or movements	
Age Appearance	Appears mature regardless of age	
Environment	Home is comfortable, cozy and warm— nothing too formal or 'precious'	
Dominant Expression	Comfort first and foremost	

HIGH SPIRITED		
OVERALL		**CHECK BOX**
Height	Under 5'3"	
Body Shape/Build	Boyish: rectangular, small and straight; compact; small boned	
Posture/Stance	Alert; perky; stands with hands on hips; rarely static, wiry, energetic	
HEAD FEATURES		
Facial Structure	Small; triangular or angled oval; small pointed chin; "apple" cheeked	
Eyes	Average sized; wide open, not heavily lidded, friendly, mischievous twinkle	
Eyebrows	Pointed or peaked	
Nose	Short and pointed; slightly upturned at tip	
Mouth	Small; peaks on top lip; "points" or expression lines at corners of mouth, crooked smile or upturned at the corners	
Hairstyle	Short and spiky; wiry curls, cornrows, shaggy layers; ponytail & bangs; short Afro; short jheri curls	
COLORING		
Overall	Natural contrast but no extremes	
Hair	Light brown, blonde, red; with age light gray or dyed highlights	
Skin	Natural; tanned, freckles; mottled	
Eyes	Hazel, blue or brown	
MANNER		
Behavior	Upbeat and unaffected	
Manner	Direct; natural; "tomboy" quality; quirky; changeable; impish	
Voice	Animated; speaks quickly; low or squeaky; slightly unruly	
Walk/Gestures	Quick movements; gawky; unrestricted; natural; "skipping" quality	
Age Appearance	Appears young	
Environment	Home is mostly just their stopping place between activities	
Dominant Expression	Would go crazy working in a cubicle	

CLASSIC		
OVERALL		**CHECK BOX**
Height	Average: 5'4"–5'7"	
Body Shape/Build	Hips and shoulders are narrow and similar in size; toned but not highly muscular	
Posture/Stance	Easily erect; poised; well-balanced	
HEAD FEATURES		
Facial Structure	Oval; symmetrical features	
Eyes	Average sized; clear, direct but not imposing gaze	
Eyebrows	Gently arched	
Nose	Average sized; straight; aquiline; unexaggerated	
Mouth	Average size; well-modeled; clean lip line; neither full and rounded nor flat lips	
Hairstyle	Clearly delineated hairline; simple and neat style (never haphazard); never extreme; modified widow's peak	
COLORING		
Overall	Medium to light	
Hair	Soft or medium shades of blonde, brown; in age, turns uniformly gray or has a dignified gray streak	
Skin	Clear; no strong contrasts; even toned and textured; if light skin, porcelain quality	
Eyes	Blue; brown; hazel	
MANNER		
Behavior	Gracious; poised; well-mannered; modest	
Manner	Harmonious refinement	
Voice	Well-modulated; pleasant; clear; laugh is slightly subdued	
Walk/Gestures	Calm, poised, controlled; dignified	
Age Appearance	Regardless of chronological age appears to be poised and mature	
Environment	Home is an elegant, refined and formal refuge	
Dominant Expression	Able to be both a leader of others and to be a fair team player	

ROMANTIC		
OVERALL		**CHECK BOX**
Height	Average: 5'4"–5'7"	
Body Shape/Build	Hourglass figure; pear-shaped figure; long legged; slightly fleshy	
Posture/Stance	Relaxed; graceful	
HEAD FEATURES		
Facial Structure	Some roundness: Heart-shaped face or softened triangular shaped face	
Eyes	Large; luminous or "smoldering" expression; long lashes; alluring; bedroom-y	
Eyebrows	Gently arched; not overly heavy or very thin	
Nose	Delicate; long, straight or slightly turned up at the end	
Mouth	Full, curved lips; lips appear slightly parted	
Hairstyle	Long; soft curls or waves; parted on the side rather than middle; cascading; partly covers one eye or side of the face; soft feminine style	
COLORING		
Overall	Skin has a "glowing" and rich quality	
Hair	Dark; golden blonde; red; not likely to let hair go gray or salt and pepper—more likely to dye it	
Skin	Supple; fine textured; clear, whether dark or light	
Eyes	Brown; dark blue; or blue/violet	
MANNER		
Behavior	Sensual mystery	
Manner	Seductive; flirtatious; charming; naturally engaging	
Voice	Soft; slightly lower pitched; feminine; tilts head when speaking or touches person spoken to	
Walk/Gestures	Graceful, languid and unhurried in gesture and movement; fluid, slow walk	
Age Appearance	Not the youthfulness of childhood, but never appears old	
Environment	Home is like a spa: luxurious; sensuous; feeling of opulence	
Dominant Expression	Secretly attracted to naughty people	

YOUTHFUL		
OVERALL		**CHECK BOX**
Height	Usually small frame; under 5'4"	
Body Shape/Build	Small boned; more fleshy than bony; roundness in elbows and knees rather than angularity	
Posture/Stance	Head tends to tilt when they speak; very expressive hands	
HEAD FEATURES		
Facial Structure	Round face; rounded cheeks and/or chin; dimples on chin or near eyes	
Eyes	Wide-eyed; very round and/or large; wide open; eyes curve down at ends	
Eyebrows	Delicate; natural arch	
Nose	Small; often button-tipped; upward tilted	
Mouth	Small mouth; rounded lips; one lip tends to be larger than the other	
Hairstyle	Generally curly; short ringlets or curls; short feathered cut; braids; sometimes bangs	
COLORING		
Overall	Fair	
Hair	Blonde, pale red or light brown; with maturity hair turns yellowish/white	
Skin	Finely textured pale undertones; pinky skin	
Eyes	Bright blue, green	
MANNER		
Behavior	Playful enthusiasm	
Manner	Demure, naive, innocent	
Voice	High pitched; giggly; upbeat; laughs a lot; doesn't hide their emotions	
Walk/Gestures	Quick; buoyant	
Age Appearance	Appears young regardless of age	
Environment	Their home is a playground (when they're not at an actual amusement park); a place for little collectibles; toys, games; stuffed animals	
Dominant Expression	Life is a party	

ANGELIC		
OVERALL		**CHECK BOX**
Height	5'6" or taller	
Body Shape/Build	Narrow hips and shoulders; slight delicate build, thin, model's or ballerina body; elongated, appearing as a "soft drip" of the body	
Posture/Stance	Graceful—ballerina-like posture	
HEAD FEATURES		
Facial Structure	Long oval or long softened angular face; often has a long neck	
Eyes	Soft expression; thinly lidded; far-away look; eyes slightly turn up at ends	
Eyebrows	Thin, pale eyebrows	
Nose	Delicate; fine boned	
Mouth	Pale in color, small; flat rather than full lips	
Hairstyle	Wispy, long and straight or long and fluffy; silken or 'cloud-like' quality	
COLORING		
Overall	Very fair—little contrast between hair and skin and eyes	
Hair	Pale blonde or strawberry blonde; with age their hair color turns golden or pale silvery/white, fine, thin hair	
Skin	Very pale, "thin" skin, porcelain	
Eyes	Pale blue or pale green; 'disappearing' pale eyelashes	
MANNER		
Behavior	Waiflike idealism; has a mystic quality	
Manner	Introspective, passive, shy, yielding, quixotic, otherworldly	
Voice	Soft light chuckle; doesn't raise voice to be heard or to make a point	
Walk/Gestures	Slow and smooth gait—seems as if floating on air	
Age Appearance	Ageless, timeless quality	
Environment	They are surrounded by vintage treasures and delicate antiques, such as etched glass, porcelain dishes, fine lace	
Dominant Expression	Appears as if from another era—or another world	

Your Totals

If your answers were almost all of one type, you will have a very easy time shopping. For the rest—and I'm guessing that's 99 percent of you, or you wouldn't have bought this book—understanding the various aspects of your body, face, and personality can help you create a more integrated, unique look. Remember, each of the descriptions is simply an *archetype,* a single note, and not the symphony that you are.

If you scored high in one of these style archetypes but just don't relate to its Dominant Quality, you may simply find that the Dominant Quality of another type deserves a little more weight in your calculations.

The more of these archetypes you embody, the more thought you'll have to put into your shopping decisions. It becomes easier with a little practice. Over time you'll find yourself gravitating to clothing and accessories that express your multiple style types in the proportion to which they reflect your features, personality, etc.

Now that you've added up your totals and discovered the archetypes that best describe you, see if you identify with—and how much you identify with—the following descriptions. Keep in mind that these descriptions, just like the archetypal seasonal colors, are of single archetype, not combinations.

Dramatic

The coloring of the archetypal Dramatic individual is often (but not always) in the Striking Contrast range: Not only can they usually wear strongly contrasting colors, they are a study in contrasts in general. They tend to have pronounced cheekbones. These are the people who are the center of their social world. Their life and friendships are often based on drama or excitement. They know important people. You won't find any shrinking violets among Dramatic types. Rather than being simply sensual, their attraction is magnetic. There's something larger-than-life about them. They may be in the public eye or the entertainment field.

Dramatic archetypes see life clearly, often in extremes, and tend to be outspoken. Accordingly, their clothing expresses no ambiguity either. The taller ones can pull off exaggerated shapes like long, tight sleeves, high turtlenecks, plunging necklines, and oversized silhouettes. Their clothing details will have substance: larger buttons—or a single large button—wider or puffy collars, larger cuffs, and wider pocket plackets. They can likely wear bold patterns or color blocks, richly piled fabrics, fake or real fur and bold animal prints. You might see them in ultrahigh boots that reach beyond the knee, or sporting spiky stilettos.

Dramatic accessories like larger bags—or those made from reflective material in white, silver, or black leather—both flat and shiny-work for them. They love to experiment with wild or exaggerated makeup and avant-garde styles in clothing, footwear, and accessories. People often consider them sophisticated, innovative and fashion leaders. Their jewelry usually includes unambiguous statement pieces like an ultramodern cocktail ring or a one-off necklace by a well-known designer.

Think Manhattan and Dubai. Dramatic types often share a natural affinity with Romantic types.

Natural

Those who represent the casual, laid-back, salt of the earth, Natural archetype are often Earthy Rich in coloring. Because they are intrinsically yang in nature, angular shapes are often a part of their bone structure. There is something of the earth mother about them but they have a sensualist's appreciation for the good things in life—good food, good friends, and happy family get-togethers. Their ease and lack of artifice inspire trust and make people feel comfortable around them.

Natural types make life choices based on comfort and very practical considerations. That goes for their attire as well. The elastic waistband and drawstring pants were invented for these types. If they absolutely have to wear a suit it will likely be somewhat relaxed, not overly constructed and made from natural fibers. Their ideal fabrics are cotton knits, corduroy, drape-y materials like viscose, suede, raw silk, and textured wool, plus slubby woven textiles. They prefer things they can just toss in the washer and dryer—as long as they don't include too much synthetic material. They likely have a collection of cozy sweaters. The wardrobe of Natural types often has animal prints, camouflage, or other patterns that represent or suggest nature themes. They are fond the great outdoors and like outdoorsy or sporty clothing. They don't go for items that say *trend*. Like old friends, they hang on to their favorite clothes for a long time.

They gravitate to rough-hewn, native, ethnic, bohemian, or hand-made jewelry and accessories, made from materials like semiprecious uncut stones, wood, or leather. Like their friends, the High Spirited types, they like boots, but theirs are most likely cowboy boots, Doc Martens, and Uggs. Moccasins and topsiders can be their everyday go-tos.

Think Berkeley, Taos, and anywhere in Alaska. Those in the Natural category tend to share some affinity with the Romantic types.

High Spirited

The coloring of the High Spirited archetype is often Lively Bright or Earthy Rich. A combination of yin and yang energies, their features are neither completely angular nor completely oval. In their personality and behavior they are slightly mischievous. Although not as theatrical as the Dramatic types, they are the life of the party and likely dance, sing, or act. They don't feel comfortable standing or sitting still for very long. Even as they age, they tend to move rather quickly. Always on the go, they seem to attract people to whatever is their latest interest.

High Spirited types are natural chameleons: Their attire and accessories are often trendy, frequently eclectic, quirky, and a little bit edgy. They're not likely to be caught dead—at least not if they have a choice—in a uniform of any kind, unless they're making an ironic statement. Details like spangles, sparkles, topstitching, rivets, and smaller fringe echo their nature, as long as they're not frilly or too precious; so do close-fitting silhouettes like pegged pants, tighter and shorter skirts, peplum tops, or short jackets and boleros.

Their energy is reflected in clothing or hairstyles that express their whimsy. Often small in stature, their textures, knits, patterns, and prints tend to be smaller in scale: checks or geometrics, small repeated patterns or thin stripes. Capris and a bateau-neck, striped shirt with ballet flats could be their daily attire. It's likely that they have a pretty healthy shoe closet—one that is often the basis of their entire wardrobe—filled with things like leopard print or sparkly flats, multicolored striped espadrilles, and ankle boots. They sometimes change clothes more than once a day because, well, it's just so much darn fun! They have a fairly quick turnover of their wardrobe. Their jewelry box is full of fun costume jewelry.

Think Hollywood and Broadway. High Spirited types share a natural affinity with the Natural and Youthful types.

Classic

The Classic archetype sits at the balance point between yin and yang—and can share affinity with almost any other type. They have a strong center and are somewhat conservative. Because they exude balance, their facial structure is likely to be an unexaggerated oval. The clothing they choose often reflects traditional qualities, in finely tailored shapes and traditional patterns like argyles, pin stripes, small polka dots, piping on trim, paisleys, and (tastefully small) logos. They are most comfortable in refined fabrics with some stiffness, like cotton poplins, worsted wools or wool flannel, gabardines, and smoother leathers—but they also can wear fine jerseys and, because of its refinement, cashmere. They just tend to look better in duller fabrics, like silk shantung or sueded silk, than in shiny, like polished cotton or satin charmeuse. Refinement is a part of their whole package. Details like fine pleats and pinwale corduroy suit them more than anything boxy, puffy, or bigger in scale. They'd likely be comfortable in some kind of uniform with simple, interchangeable pieces.

Classic archetypes are frequently considered chic but never flamboyant; they don't have the über-sophistication of a Dramatic type. Since they are preppy and aristocratic by nature they never feel comfortable in baggy, wrinkled, or overly revealing clothes. They're not likely to hop on the trend bandwagon either. When they update their wardrobe, it's most likely with a new flattering color or pattern rather than an asymmetrical or outlandish shape. Shawl collars, rather than very rounded or deeply cut ones, suit them best. They buy quality items that last. Their shoe closet is consistent year-to-year and often features simple, elegant pumps, plain or colored sneakers, and sleek, minimally adorned flats. The younger Classic types avoid looking dowdy (Classic is, after all, a mature look) by sporting higher heels and brighter colors, and by showing a little more skin. Their jewelry box is made up of timeless pieces, often inherited, like pearls and gemstone ear studs. You probably won't find much in their collection that dangles or is overly complicated. And they'll never shop cheap.

Think Boston and Washington, D.C.—and many of our political leaders.

Romantic

This is the archetype that, regardless of size or height, is considered sexy and alluring. There's just something in those eyes! They also tend to have a little more meat on their bones than some of the other types. (Makes them juicier!) Romance, being yin in nature, suggests some roundness in their bone structure, mouth, or eyes. They have a subtle but magnetic personality that both men and women find attractive. Their clothing choices enhance their innate sensuality. Fabrics with a yummy hand like velvet, satin, and fur are naturals for them, as are those that speak of mystery, like dark lace and rich florals. They can even get away with something as outrageous as a feather boa. If they wear knits they're more likely to be the body-hugging, tighter weaves—very fine wool and cashmere—rather than large or slubby weaves. They never wear boxy-shaped garments or outfits. Fitted pencil skirts or those that have some fullness, e.g., gathers or bouffant styles, show off their figure, as do off-the-shoulder, deep-V, or sweetheart necklines. Draped collars and fabrics that suggest body lines rather than conceal them emphasize the innate femininity of the Romantic. When they buy loungewear it's likely made of velvet, satin, or cashmere. Rest assured it's not sweat clothes. They can wear ruffles and cinched waists. They can expose a fair amount of cleavage and never look like they're trying too hard. These things simply reflect their nature.

Their outerwear is never too outdoorsy, since they like to show their figure. They lead with their heart (that "kept woman" in the gem-encrusted bustier sitting in the box seat at the opera is most likely a Romantic type). They're also the ones who can wear things like feathered mules, d'Orsay pumps, and ankle-strap sandals. Their jewelry box is rarely timid. It may well include cascades of diamonds or bold gemstones.

Think Paris, Seville and San Francisco. Romantics have a natural affinity with Natural and Dramatic types.

Youthful

Those who fall in this adventurous, lively archetype just never seem to age. Bubbly characters that they are, they express the yin quality of movement through round facial features. They enjoy people of all ages but particularly love younger people because they relate to them so easily... and vice versa. Maybe that's because they're willing to engage in fantasy and adventure long after other types would have given these things up. Their joyful laugh, idealism and innocence define them. Because of their intrinsic innocence and naïveté it's hard for anyone to pick a fight with them. And because they often find the humor in many situations, they rarely make enemies.

Youthfuls gravitate to clothing that has some kind of light-hearted detail or youthful shape: rounded collars, empire waists, gathers at the shoulders, smaller ruffles, puckering, bows and tied waistbands, rounded-rather than pointed-toe shoes and Mary Janes. They often wear endearing accessories, like animal pins on a collar or hat. The patterns they choose are generally smaller in size and can include charming details like polka dots, checks, flowers, and small plaids. Their sweater patterns are constructed with smaller weaves of what are classics for them: cables, popcorn stitches, and Fair Isle patterns. These are the types that can wear amusing statement or fan T-shirts long past the time most adults can get away with it. Even a tongue-in-cheek image like a smiley face can look natural on a Youthful type. They sparkle in crisp fabrics like polished cotton, seersucker, gingham, eyelet, taffeta, and even peek-a-boo weaves like macramé and lace. Small amounts of reflective materials like patent leather can suit them too, especially in shoes. In fact, any shoe made with their favorite fabrics—lace, gingham canvas, or cut-out shapes of any kind, say *youthful*. They can wear amusing earrings and jangly or delicately embellished jewelry and won't look ridiculous, regardless of age.

Think Disneyland, English country cottages, fantasy comics. They share a natural affinity with the High Spirited and Angelic archetypes.

Angelic

This archetype's feet barely touch the ground. Women of this type may have many spiritual, philosophical, or religious interests and aspirations or be described as not having much interest in the material world at all. The bone structure of an Angelic, the most yin of all the archetypes, tends to have some curving feature, such as a slightly round or oval shape, or if more pronounced, an angular oval. They tend to avoid conflict at all cost. They were, or wish they could have been, a '60s flower child. Many are tall or waif-thin—hence the model-like quality they project. In fact, the taller ones can often be found on fashion runways, as they offer the drama of height with a gentle personality that doesn't overshadow the clothing.

Angelic types can wear tie-dye, amorphous, iridescent, or ombre patterns. They feel comfortable in featherweight fabrics like cotton voile or chiffon and very finely woven drapey knits. They gravitate to clothes that aren't overly constructed or constraining, nor overly revealing, but because of their innate modesty, they can easily wear diaphanous fabrics without looking cheap. They can also wear extremely soft knits like angora or mohair sweaters, shimmery fabrics and even feathers! (What would an angel be without her feathers?) Their otherworldliness is attracted to pieces that recall another era, as time itself has an ephemeral quality. Their closets contain layered or flowing pieces; tops and skirts or dresses with asymmetrical hems; palazzo-style rather than closely fitted pants; and tops with bell-shaped or kimono sleeves. Much of their wardrobe has an overall vintage feel.

The jewelry of Angelics also has an old-fashioned, antique quality: rose gold and pink pearls, mother-of-pearl or opal, delicate and intricate metalwork. Their handbag, if they carry one, can be a knit or macramé with metallic threads, lightweight and sparkly or pearlescent. In the fashion magazines you'll see Angelics carrying dramatically constructed oversize handbags, simply because they have the height to carry off the look. But it's just as likely they don't like to lug those around in real life. If they wear shoes at all, they're likely to be silver, gold, or mesh and often sandals, unless the weather is cold, in which case you can find them wearing fluffy shearling-lined boots.

Think New Age. Think Utopia or the lost city of Atlantis. These types have a natural affinity with the Youthful types, and sometimes, if they are very tall, with the Dramatic ones, as their otherworldliness can be extremely eye-catching—coming full circle from most yin to most yang.

So there are the seven basic style archetypes. Now let's look at some combinations of these archetypes to see how they have been translated in popular magazines, blogs, and possibly your own wardrobe.

Androgynous: A combination of Natural with a tad of Classic; the uniform is menswear fabrics and styling that can actually appear rather sexy.

Avant-Garde: Primarily Dramatic with a minimalist Classic element.

Bohemian: A combination of Romantic and laid-back Natural; can handle a greater volume of fabric, combinations of patterns, colorful jewelry in multiple strands, gypsy-like dangly earrings or stacks of colorful bracelets.

Exotic: A combination of highly Dramatic with some of the alluring quality of the Romantic. Not as earthy as the bohemian types, more drama than femme fatale types, something a little held back and mysterious.

Femme Fatale: Also Dramatic and Romantic, but with more Romantic than Exotic; furs, satins, highly revealing cuts, e.g., a high slit in a long dress, shiny and/or wavy hair with an exaggerated style.

Goth: Very Dramatic and Angelic; slightly otherworldly and dark (a combination of extremes, and that's exactly the intention).

Girly: Youthful combined with Romantic; an element of softness such as furry sweaters, soft ruffles, feathers, flirty hemlines that move back and forth when you walk, short soft waves in hair, more playful fabrics and small-scale patterns.

Grunge (a "style" that rears its head every few decades): Natural combined with Dramatic; army boots or other intentionally unfeminine shoes, torn jeans, layers of loose tees, a vest, plaid jackets or shirts; a rumpled overall look. (Honestly, do you really want to look like that?)

Ladylike or Demure: Classic, often featured on an hourglass figure; simple silhouettes, defined waistlines, skin more covered than revealed, often some vintage elements—a throwback to '50s or '60s fashion, sometimes minimalist structures in garments and accessories.

Minimalist: Classic with a slightly Dramatic edge (the reverse proportion of these elements in Avant-Garde). Clothes are often architectural in shape, with a bare-bones cleanness of line.

Rock 'n' Roll: Dramatic with an High Spirited mischievous edge; exaggerated silhouettes such as skinny jeans, short-shorts, edgy leather jackets, or ultrahigh artsy shoes, and dramatic makeup. A tad Romantic with things like see-through fabrics or exposed skin thrown in for sexiness.

Sporty: A Classic and Natural blend; traditional silhouettes in more natural fibers; can also describe Preppy.

Vintage: Angelic mixed with a bit of Romantic; a combination of feminine, sentimental nostalgia that speaks of another era; delicate ornamentation and design.

Chic: Ah, yes, chic … what almost everyone likes to be considered. Well, that's the entire topic of our next chapter.

If you still find it difficult to clearly identify where you fit in the above categories, or if you fit into so many categories that you're still confused, Chapter 7—*Make New Friends*, will help you find some assistance in fine-tuning your personal style.

Shopping with Your Style in Mind

If you find only a small portion of a particular archetype in your features and personality, that quality should be represented in equally minimal proportions, by something like an accessory. Just as with coloring, the idea is to emphasize your primary style type and then integrate the other elements proportionately.

Here's an example. If you're mostly a laid-back, Natural type but have pixie-like High Spirited personality, you'd want to temper that crunchy granola with a little zing by wearing shorter skirts or jingly jewelry, or even a face-hugging, shaggy or curly hairdo. If you've found that you're pretty much a Classic in features and body shape but have some round elements thrown in, such as large round eyes or "apple" cheeks, you can wear tailored cuts with rounded details—like Peter Pan collars and curved lapels, or jewelry with some round shape. In fact, echoing the shapes of your features with the details in your clothing creates a nice sense of visual harmony.

But keep your age in mind when implementing these guidelines. Regardless of how much of the Youthful type you reflect in your features, detailing like little ruffles and larger bows work only for the very young. Stick to the silhouettes that work for your body (see Chapter 6) and carry the youthful style through in patterns and the shape of your accessories.

Bear in mind that, just as with colors, there are going to be years when what's in style isn't meant for you. In those times, take a deep breath, find an accessory that takes you fashion forward, and stick with what has worked for you in the past.

As we touched on this in the previous chapter, a common mistake is to automatically identify a particular color palette with a particular style. Yes, there are some natural associations between certain seasons and certain types: Dramatic and Romantic with winter, High Spirited and Youthful with spring, Classic or Angelic with summer, and Natural with fall. But now you understand that there's a lot more to style than just your coloring. It's very important to pay attention to the distinction between your specific style types and your coloring, especially in those years when designers haven't.

Here's one more important point: It's just a fact that most women want to be considered Youthful and/or Romantic. If your style types pretty much exclude those categories (that's me) you can create the effect of youthfulness with some of your lighter, or more pastel-like colors and the effect of romance by wearing any of your reds, corals, or pinks.

When considering a garment, scrutinize it in light of what you know about your basic style elements, and then ask yourself the following questions:

> ✤ *Does the overall silhouette, detailing, neckline, sleeve design, and skirt/pants shape match the spirit of and the inherent shapes in my style types?*

Here's a design clue: The more yang your style types the more you can favor straight lines and angles. Straight lines suggest repose, a yang characteristic. The more yin your style types, the more you can favor curved shapes and lines. Curved lines and shapes suggest motion, a yin characteristic.

Translating that into clothing means that those with a lot of yang can wear anything that creates an angled line, e.g., V-necks, halters, surplices, and straight boatnecks, patterns with linear or angular designs. They can wear traditional set-in sleeves or cap sleeves and, depending on the tone of their arms, they can go sleeveless.

Those with more yin will be able to wear rounded and oval shapes and things that suggest movement, e.g., ruffles, sweetheart necklines, rounded collars, scalloped edges, and rounded or puffed sleeves.

✤ *Does the fabric texture and weave speak of my true nature?*

If you're delicate-boned, can you really carry off that heavy tweed coat or suit? Perhaps, if the scale of the weave works for you or you're tall. Generally, more texture and oversized structure are characteristics of a yang style. Height suggests yang. Likewise, if you're athletic and energetic, does that flowing, diaphanous skirt really complement you? Again, it very well might—most of us are multiple types. But it depends on your body shape (see Chapter 6) and your features. Good to ask yourself the question for confirmation.

✤ *Does the pattern or print match my personality?*

If you're over 5'8" and very Dramatic, do tiny polka dots speak to your true nature? If you look terrific in a gentle rose print, does that color-blocked or bold woven fabric reflect your personality?

✤ *What does this garment say about me, and am I happy saying that?*

Overall, you want to express harmony between your inward self and your outward self. Unless you're dressing for a Halloween party, the answers to all these questions ought to be yes!

Shopping Serendipity

There's an almost magical key to finding a perfect garment that appropriately reflects your entire personality and style types. It involves the same process required in any creative endeavor. Experts in the fields of science, art, and business will tell you that their best ideas arrive when they least expect it. However, they have created a fertile ground—enriched by a great deal of study and information—on which those ideas can germinate. Gaining knowledge and then letting go is the delightful process toward intuitive discovery.

You've now gained a lot of information about your style. Revisit it periodically, then **let it go**.

Keep adding to your arsenal of self-knowledge, and your ideal clothing choices will gradually become second nature. But after taking in all the above, here's an important point:

Don't obsess on trying to find the perfect garment that matches all the aspects of your style every time you shop.

You can make yourself crazy by constantly second-guessing your choices: *Is this expressing the right amount of all my style types and my coloring?* You just might actually find a garment that meets all your color and style criteria, and that will be a revelation! When you do find that garment or accessory that makes you say *yes!* from the core of your being, nobody— no salesperson, no shopping buddy, no significant other—will have to explain it to you. You will just *know*. And every time you wear it you'll feel confident, happy, and fabulous. But if you find something that makes you happy but doesn't exactly suit all your style types wear it with joy! Joy shows on your face and can be the very best stylist.

What to Change, What to Keep, What to Enhance

I am about to embark on perhaps the most controversial area of personal style: plastic surgery. Clearly, a major component of style is our facial features. Some people experience emotional turmoil because they were born with features they consider out of proportion to their size and to the rest of their bone structure. I'll be the last person to tell them they shouldn't change a feature that will make them feel more integrated and whole.

But keep this in mind; as we mature and grow into our faces, sometimes we discover that the same features we once considered unattractive are exactly what defines our beauty. I've seen this to be true with women and men who contemplated plastic surgery and then changed their minds. A woman friend of mine briefly considered rhinoplasty (a nose job) and then decided against it. I think it was absolutely the right decision for her. Her overall facial bone structure and the shape of her mouth created great aesthetic balance and classic beauty. A smaller nose would have ruined the integrity of who she is and would have made the rest of her face look out of proportion. An actor I knew had a nose job and found he couldn't get work—so he had it redone back to how it was before the surgery and landed a job in a TV series that's still earning him royalties!

If you look at classic portraits from the past few centuries you'll see very different types of beauty that, today, would have sent many of those people to a plastic surgeon's office. What a loss to the world that would have been. Before you take on any major change in your features, look for photographs, paintings, and images of someone whose features mirror your own and find the beauty in those images. It can change your entire idea about how you see yourself. Is it possible that a feature you consider fat or fleshy is seen by others as sensual and warm? Does someone else consider your strong jaw a sign of your sexy strength and power? Could it be that someone else sees your smaller lips as playful or cute? With that information, plus an understanding of your individual colors and style, you just might find out how beautiful you already are.

Purists (and a lot of them are either Dramatic or Natural types) argue that plastic surgery is never necessary and that we should just learn to embrace all of ourselves as we are. They also argue that many people, once they have plastic surgery, feel so different that they longer know who they are. Both statements are true … for some people. So it's wise to spend some time imagining your life with the physical change you are contemplating before you actually commit to it. [By the way, I'm not referring here to a correctable abnormality; that's a completely different situation.]

Now, if after taking all this into consideration you still find some aspect of your face that bothers you to the point that you decide to have it changed understand that the change itself may be part of your personal growth. Sometimes we just have to put issues of our appearance behind us before we can move forward into deeper territory.

When electing to have plastic surgery it's crucial to find a surgeon who is an artist—someone who can design the change so that it harmonizes with the rest of your face. It's always tempting to just go for the features of the more youthful, yin-type face. It's also very popular to bring a photograph of a young starlet in to the surgeon's office and say, "Make me look like *that!*" But holding onto youth—especially someone else's—when it's not a natural part of your style and expression may just end up saying *immaturity*. A long, angular, or large nose can be made into one with more classic proportions if the rest of your bone structure will support that change. If your face is very angular or your features are larger, a tiny, upturned nose may look out of place. A receding chin can be augmented to have more oomph as long as it balances with your existing nose and cheekbones. The point is to bring things into balance and congruity, not disharmony.

As far as surgical body sculpting is concerned, I'm not even going to go there. (A shocking number of teenagers are having breast augmentation these days.) But the same principle applies. Do it only if it's causing you anguish and then live with the idea before going under the knife.

Remember, personal style is not something to be bought or adopted. It's to be recognized and unfolded, and then simply emphasized. In her wonderful (if dated) 1950s book *The Dress Doctor*, famed Hollywood costumer Edith Head tells a story about one of her early clients, actress and playwright Cornelia Otis Skinner. Skinner described how she chose the roles she played: "You don't try a character that you can't believe or that the audience won't believe; you shouldn't in real life either."

If during your transformation from caterpillar to butterfly you find yourself in need of a little self-love, I can recommend a wonderful book by author Marcy Shimoff: *Happy for No Reason.* When I flip through this book, the chapter titles alone remind me of what is important for that day: "Forgive," "Focus on the Solution," "Incline Your Mind Toward Joy." It's also chock-full of practical advice ("Drink more water!" One of the most important beauty tips of all time, by the way) and uplifting stories that will help you learn how to be healthy and happy for a lifetime.

Ask yourself: *Do my clothes echo my features and personality; my true self?*

From Style to Stylish

4

The purpose of this chapter is to help you create a wardrobe that is functional, easy, and attractive. The principles of stylishness are applicable to every style type, body shape, and coloring. So let's look a little deeper into the concept of what it means to be stylish.

In the world of high fashion, stylishness implies *cutting-edge*. But since this book is about the real world we're going to examine

> "Fashion passes, style remains."
> — *COCO CHANEL*

stylishness from the vantage point of your own closet. So let's make a distinction here. Being stylish is not the same as being fashionable. High fashion is art, and art—especially the avant-garde—is often a dramatized commentary on collective consciousness, cultural trends, and world events. (And sometimes it's just a reflection of the designer's personal life that year.)

Chanel's Karl Lagerfeld says, "Fashion is ephemeral, dangerous, and unfair." An exciting concept, of course, but it's all the more reason to look at high fashion with a somewhat skeptical eye. By the time those cutting-edge ideas make it down market to those of us who live in the real world, they're usually translated into something more wearable and flattering to a woman's body. And, more affordable. But that still doesn't mean a particular trend is right for you. One person's version of very classic might just be another's sort of dowdy.

Let's look at some of the traditional synonyms for the term *stylish*: sophisticated, refined, chic, smart, and classy. We'll take them one at a time.

Sophistication implies a kind of elegance or understatement. It's a quality that can be achieved fairly easily. Sophisticated clothing suggests garments that are well tailored, have fine or well-made details (that means they're not overdone or overly fussy), are made from natural or refined fabrics and are beautifully cut or draped. The words *refinement* and *class* imply polish and good taste, a demonstration that you take care in how you present yourself to the world. And *smart*? I think that speaks for itself. Dressing in your colors, with your personality and style in mind, shows how smart you are.

And then there's chic. Chic is the opposite of gaudy, tawdry, or overdone. Sometimes just a simple white blouse, rolled-up sleeves, a pair of perfectly tailored pants, well-made flats or heels, and an armful of bracelets can say *chic*. It certainly worked for style icon Babe Paley. Chic dressing implies clean, beautifully tailored lines and includes staple looks that can complement any body type, any style type, and any color harmony. It generally implies an uncomplicated look and line in—sorry, but I have to say it—neutral colors. Still, keep in mind that chic does not have to mean safe or boring. Beautifully tailored, refined clothing is rarely boring. And a proportionately sized but bold accessory can take that most classic staple and turn it into something that is extremely chic.

Now if you look at many people who work in the fashion industry you'll notice that their day-to-day uniform can often be much like the rest of ours. As often as not you'll find them in a T-shirt or sweater and jeans rather than the latest fashions. But those jeans and that T-shirt will fit beautifully and be well-made. So what sets their uniform apart?

Details, Details, Details ...

Refined details like impeccable fit, clean or invisible hemming, and perfectly executed seams add a sense of polish and say *quality*. It also bears repeating that fabric is a dead giveaway about the quality of the garment. You can wear the funkiest of jeans, but add a beautiful cashmere sweater and it instantly reads stylish—and hip. Both the drape and hand (feel and weight) of a fabric project what it is made of, even at a distance. Natural fabrics—linen, linen/silk blends, silk, wool, cotton, cotton/silk blends, cashmere, fine suede, and leather—are the refined staples that can look elegant for a lifetime.

Although in general, synthetic fabrics say *cheaper*, many designers are using new blends of natural and synthetic fibers that can look extremely elegant. Fabrics with viscose or bamboo (natural but atypical) also have a substantial feel and tend to last longer and look great even after many launderings or cleanings. Even the addition of a small amount of Lycra can make some fabrics look more flattering and last longer. (This, from someone who wouldn't touch even the tiniest amount of synthetic fiber for many years ... age tends to change one's mind about stretchy material.) And lately some of the faux leathers and furs can fool the most discerning eye. I was prepared to pay several hundred dollars for a dark-green leather biker jacket recently, only to discover it was, in fact, vinyl. And on sale for $40! Well, *that* was a no-brainer.

But generally, high quality comes with a price. I learned about this from a most unusual source. Back in the days of hippie chic, the early 70s, I sat in a room with several hundred young would-be meditation teachers awaiting every bit of wisdom imparted by our teacher, Maharishi Mahesh Yogi. One day, instead of expounding on the finer points of consciousness development, he instead gave us fashion advice. That's right. A guru in a silk robe taught me one of the most valuable shopping lessons I ever learned. The talk went something like this: if you have something important to share with the world and you want to be taken seriously, the way in which you present yourself is important. Therefore, he concluded:

"Wear the highest quality and the best-cut clothing you can afford."

In summary, precise tailoring, few distracting details, and quality fabrics say *stylish*.

Start Simply

After drilling into your head for the last three chapters that you are unique, I'm going to throw you a curve. Stay with me! Fashion books, designer blogs, and personal shoppers advise even the most quirky or avant-garde style type to start with simple, classic pieces in their wardrobe. Because the Classic style archetype sits at the midpoint on the yin/yang spectrum of style types, it has to reflect the balance between them. This is why dressing in a chic manner implies dressing with what is considered classic elegance—balance and tastefulness, two qualities of the Classic style type. It's just a very smart, practical, and economical idea to include some of the classic pieces, often in neutrals, in your wardrobe.

There is a really good reason for this: These pieces can anchor more individual or unique pieces and/or pull an outfit together. This classic core of your wardrobe also makes getting dressed at a moment's notice a lot simpler. It's a great strategy to avoid style fatigue—that mental block that sends us into comfortable, but not always flattering, clothes.

If we look at fashion over time we will notice that what survives has an eternal quality: simple, uncomplicated silhouettes, un-fussy prints in small to moderate scale, just a few statement accessories, and hemlines—in both slacks and skirts or dresses—that suggest rather than expose. These are considered the classic, chic elements in design.

Among the commonly understood classic garments that suit everyone are such things as the trench coat, the little black dress (LBD) and the white tailored blouse. The LBD can actually be any dark, neutral color within your color range and that you can dress up or down—so long as it's beautifully tailored and in a fine fabric. (Can you guess I'm a

FROM STYLE TO STYLISH

little black averse? I don't wear it very much. Ah well, I surrender that aversion a little bit later in this chapter.)

A well-made, neutral-colored skirt suit and/or pant suit can be the basis of multiple outfits. The classic white tailored blouse is something that can look both sexy and refined. And, as not all of us can wear brightest white-white, it can be in one of your lighter neutrals—light tan, cream, ecru, even palest pink. Some of the other classics include a good cashmere sweater, a tailored pair of slacks, and a simple pencil skirt at the appropriate knee length for your body and age.

Now, the fact is that classics are reinterpreted a bit every few years. Some years they might have a tougher edge and some years a softer one. Some years they will incorporate color or unusual fabrics or textures. Keep your eye out for one of those distinctive takes on one of the classics that suits your unique style. Maybe your trench coat will be in red leather instead of tan, black, or navy. Maybe it will be iridescent or patterned! (Both of which I saw this year.) If you're a romantic through and through, maybe that white tailored blouse isn't cotton but a yummy silk or viscose blend. Or if you're a Natural type you might find your classic blouse in heavy linen, maybe with something like hand-made wooden buttons.

If your style or lifestyle dictates little or no need for a traditional suit, your version might be a pair of quality trousers or a skirt with something other than a blazer, such as a peplum jacket, a short belted trench ... or maybe a three-quarter-sleeve moto jacket in suede or supple leather. (That last one was for High Spirited types; they often have to express their artsy streak or they come off looking bland.)

It may take time to find just what you're looking for—something that meets your criteria for classic within your style type—but it will be well worth it. In the interim, when in doubt, stick with the traditional versions, as they will project balance, harmony, and, well—taste.

NOTE: If you want to know what all the "classics" are, there's a charming little book called *The One Hundred: A Guide to the Pieces Every Stylish Woman Must Own* written by Nina Garcia, creative director of *Marie Claire* magazine. (In my opinion she had to stretch a bit to come to the 100 mark, but still ...)

LBD Style Tutorial

Taking the seven basic style types, we can play around with the idea of what kind of little black dress (make sure it's *your* black) might suit your primary style. For those whose coloring is washed out by black, wearing a splash of color in your lipstick or other makeup can liven up your face. Keep in mind that a classic, tailored V-neck or a modified boat neck on a well-fitted, not overly clinging, sheath complements nearly every body and style. That is why Diane von Furstenberg's jersey wrap dresses have stood the test of time. If you have toned arms you can carry off a sleeveless style. If you feel equally comfortable in two or even three style types, the ideas for each category can likely work for you as well.

Here are some ideas for silhouettes and details of LBDs suitable for the seven style archetypes with an illustration of one possibility for each. [FYI: Many of the midlevel retailers now have web pages dedicated exclusively to their LBDs filled with nearly every silhouette you can imagine.]

Dramatic: Your LBD can have strong and bold lines— an exaggerated slit, dramatic neckline, one shoulder, dropped shoulder seams or kimono sleeves or highly structured architectural/minimalist lines.

Natural: Your LBD will have a relaxed silhouette in a drape-y or more richly textured fabric, with an angled or an asymmetrical neckline (avoid anything too round in shape) and few, if any, details.

High Spirited: Your LBD could be a little sexier than classic, e.g., a fitted sheath with an off-shoulder, one shoulder, cap sleeve, or an asymmetrical neckline.

Classic: Your LBD can be a fitted sheath, V-neck, with uncomplicated details, and sleeveless, three-quarter, or longer sleeves.

Youthful: Your LBD can have a slightly higher or empire waistline, a round or ruffled (small) neckline, a dirndl skirt shape, short sleeves or be sleeveless, and have small details like puckering, shirring, or gathering at the arms, shoulders or bodice. Lace details or lace fabric work well too.

Romantic: Your LBD can be draped, have cascading ruffles, a sweetheart neckline or one that flaunts your décolletage, shirring at the bust or waistline, a lower cut in the back, bias cut throughout, or of clingy fabrics like satin or jersey.

Angelic: Your LBD can be in sheer fabrics that aren't overly revealing. If long-sleeved, it can have straight or bell-shaped sleeves and if not in a classical cut, fluttery or cascading hemlines.

Style Versus Costume

Being stylish means projecting an image that is tasteful and appropriate for the environment you're in—one that is unique to you, but not campy or overdone. That takes some objectivity.

When your outfit strays from an organic, natural expression of who you are, sometimes an attempt at stylishness can stray into the realm of costume. Now if you are auditioning for a role on Broadway or attending a Comic-Con convention it's appropriate to dress for a specific character or type. Otherwise, a look that's not *you* can overwhelm the company you want to keep.

So ask yourself a few questions:

* ❖ *Who am I when I wear this? Is that the person I feel like inside?*
* ❖ *Who am I trying to impress/influence?*
* ❖ *Is this more tries-too-hard vs. effortless chic?*

Nobody's judging you—you may want to make a splash, and that might be totally congruent with your inner experience. But they're still good questions to ask yourself before you step away from the mirror and out into the world.

Aging with Style

One of my favorite Grace Morton quotes is: "Prettiness is an attribute of the young. Beauty is an ageless quality." A constant theme in stories about the eternal, elegant style of French women—particularly older French women—has to do with the way they carry themselves. French culture celebrates a life of experience, and they celebrate those who have lived it as well. (This is also true for those lovely, earthy Italian women.) You see it in the way they walk, with subtle grace and sensuality, never hurried. They exude the one beauty enhancement that can't be bought: self-love. Their expression, their carriage, the meticulous care that goes into that *effortless* chic all say, "You can't help but look at me because I'm fabulous—and I know it." Wouldn't it be wonderful if all of us, as we aged, thought of ourselves this way?

Sophia Loren said, "Beauty is in the eye of the beheld." And as designer Yves St. Laurent put it: "What is important in a dress is the woman who is wearing it."

French women talk about two regimens from which they will not deviate: maintaining steady weight—no yo-yo diets—and vigilant care of their skin. They prefer to wear less makeup so that their natural beauty shines through. (Very young teenagers in France already use anti-aging skin care products.) Those older women who do get work done aim to have it look as though nothing major has been done at all, rather than suddenly appearing 20 years younger. And they *never* try to dress like their daughters. It's a lesson we would all do well to heed. If you embrace aging with élan, your personal style can show how comfortable you are in your own skin, and how savvy you are about the way you look.

When done tastefully, stylishness can also say *hip*. This can be difficult if you have teenagers at home. Kids believe they've cornered the market on what's hip and new. God forbid you follow a trend when it suits your basic style! (Teens can be brutal when they feel the traditional parent-child roles are getting mixed up.) You certainly don't have to dress like Ma Kettle just to avoid bugging the kids. However, it's just a matter of good taste to adapt a new fashion—if it's appropriate for your style types—in a way that works with your age and stature. Remember, you don't want to look like a teenager at 50.

So, how to do that? Well, it's not all that complicated. Lately you'll see magazines that feature a particular garment or style and then demonstrate how it can be worn by women in their 20s, 30s, 40s, 50s, and up. They often get it wrong because they can't possibly take into consideration the individual style facets of each reader. Still, you will notice some consistent patterns: the younger the model, the more skin they show, the more accessories they wear, the more dressed-down the ensemble, the more style and color rules are broken—often charmingly. As they move up the age scale you will notice greater modesty, a more pulled-together look, fewer, more expensive or tasteful accessories and more refined detail and tailoring. (Remember, as we age, we become more yang, a mature quality.)

This simply echoes what should be the natural arc of our lives. In our youth most of us are trying to attract a partner—on a shoestring budget. Hence, the skin and all the shiny things that say; "Hey! Look at me!" As we mature, our clothing choices represent ourselves to our community or workplace as more self-aware and grounded. As we near retirement we generally know who we are. If we've done all right for ourselves we have the disposable income to emphasize our style with panache and taste. If we've got good sense we cover up the parts that time and gravity have made a little less appealing.

Still, after all that, I have one more rant—and a plea. Many of the older women I interviewed for this book expressed frustration about shopping for something sophisticated and age-appropriate. What they consistently told me was that dresses with longer sleeves or that simply covered the knee were often boring, shapeless, or in dark colors (those darker colors are something the French would highly approve of, by the way) or were made only for those who could afford couture. Are you listening out there, designers? This is a *huge* demographic you're missing! Frankly, I'm hoping this book helps jump-start the dialog on designing for the older, sophisticated shopper at a reasonable price point.

For now, my advice to these ladies is this: Don't limit yourself. Check out your local boutiques. They often have things you won't find in department stores. You may just come across a new up-and-coming designer whose clothing works for you, both in cut and style. Also, stay open to the possibility of finding something at a store you wouldn't ordinarily consider or that you think is only for young people. You may be happily surprised at what you'll find at places like Uniqlo, Zara's and H&M. My two current favorite and most flattering dresses are from H&M.

There's often a tendency to opt for comfort as we age. [Note: Comfort means different things to different style types, e.g., a pure Classic type will feel comfortable in a tailored suit for the rest of her life.] There's nothing wrong that—you've earned it. Just avoid making comfort such a priority that you throw style out the window. Here are a few styling suggestions to help you look attractive as you get older, regardless of your individual style type.

* Move into more sophisticated silhouettes and details. Leave anything too fussy or cutesy, such as overly youthful prints and fabrics, excessive fringe, and the wilder statement t-shirts, to the young adults or kids.

* If you want something sparkly or sexy, look for it in an accessory or blouse rather than a full-length piece.

* To add a little edge to your wardrobe wearing something

in a high-quality leather or suede—a jacket, trench, or skirt, particularly in one of your unusual neutrals—can take you fashion forward without making it look as though you're trying too hard. Leather pants work best for those who have a lot of the Dramatic style type regardless of age. The same goes for excessive ornamentation: long fringe, studding, multiple zippers.

❖ Animal print, particularly leopard, is one of those things that you can wear in small or large amounts in anything from a clutch to a blouse, dress or even outerwear. Just stay within your style line silhouette, and don't layer animal prints.

❖ If you're wearing a classic suit, give yourself a waistline: Add a belt, tuck in your blouse, or wear a fitted jacket that nips in at the waist. Avoid jackets, pantsuits, or dresses that turn you into a shapeless rectangle or a box, or have them tailored to give you some shape. Sometimes all it takes to make an unflattering item more hip is a seamstress with a good eye. (There's more about this in Chapter 8.)

❖ If you just don't like your waistline, or don't have much of one, the newer minimalist silhouettes that skim the body are very flattering for mature women. Just make sure you follow the guidelines in Chapters 6 and 8 about body shape, proportion and scale.

❖ Pick a skirt length that flatters your legs. I haven't seen anyone over the age of 30 who looks very attractive in a mid calf skirt unless it's worn with boots. And *never* wear an A-line that ends mid calf! That goes for all ages. A garment that ends at mid-calf implies that your entire leg is that wide. (Project Runway's charming sartorial guru Tim Gunn also cautions about mid calf capris and especially baggy mid calf cargo pants. They flatter no one, but are especially unattractive on older women.) Don't go higher than two inches above the knee, and then only if you've got great legs. If you're not sure what your ideal hemline is, here's a preview of Chapter 6: check out www.fashionfitformula.com.

❖ If your upper arms are toned, why not wear something sleeveless? If they aren't and it bothers you, a blouse or top with elbow-length, three-quarter, or wrist-length sleeves will hide flabby or parched-skin upper arms.

❖ If your legs are great but you're not pleased with some aspect of them (sagging skin over your knees, varicose veins) make darker or opaque stockings and/or leggings a part of your wardrobe.

❖ Unless you're a something of a natural Bohemian type who can wear multiple ethnic pieces or an High Spirited type who can wear playful costume jewelry, save up and splurge on fewer but well-made accessories. Think: less is more.

A Final Note About Being Stylish and Fashion-Forward

Life is about change and evolution. Most of us love buying at least something every season that makes us feel like we're keeping up with the times—growing, and not stagnating. A new color (that's still in your palette) in a blouse, accessory, or print can punch up your classics. Combining a new leather jacket with your classic suit skirt or wearing your suit blazer with a new pair of jeans in one of your more unusual neutrals colors can instantly make you feel fashionable, stylish and unique.

It's gratifying that fashion editors are finally recognizing there are a number of different style types out there. So when you look at the newest, hottest thing, keep in mind your fashion style types, your age, and your coloring. You will likely find that there are at least a few wonderful new pieces that work for you and that bring your wardrobe up to date.

Ask yourself: *Am I chic, elegant, and fashion forward—within my unique style?*

Shop for Your Lifestyle

5

This is a brief chapter but an extremely important one: We're going to be looking at your lifestyle as the basis for building your wardrobe. Shopping for the real you should always be an inside-to-outside job and nowhere is that more evident than when examining lifestyle.

As a child I used to tell my mother that I could live in sweatpants and T-shirts all year long. That paints a picture of the Natural style type. You can guess that comfort and nature are important in my home and my lifestyle. A clean look was also important to me. That's a Classic style staple, which I also have in equal measure. And I loved to play dress-up in front of the mirror because I also have a good dose of the High Spirited type. But comfort was always my first priority.

I think that's why I became a nonfiction writer. I sit down to my computer in a comfortable combination of pants and a top. My work requires me to speak with people on the phone, do research in the library or on the internet, occasionally taking a break to pull dandelions or walk the dog. My world is pretty unadorned. I don't have much need for power suits or LBDs or even pencil skirts.

Romance novelists, on the other hand, are a different breed entirely. Just look at the dust jackets of their books. They are often photographed wearing flowing gowns, ruffled collars, or cashmere twin sets. Many of the women fiction writers I know are more Dramatic and Romantic in their internal and external worlds. They live in a created reality, ripe with dramatic characters and faraway places. They attend cocktail parties. Their writing spaces are filled with gilt and flowers and potpourri. My office has a Craftsman-style desk and a chair.

Of course it's natural to engage in a little lifestyle fantasy from time to time, and a shopping expedition can be just the means for that kind of escape.

This scenario might sound familiar: You're browsing through the racks of your favorite store (or the formals at Ross Dress for Less) and you suddenly find a perfect evening gown in the perfect color, style, and fit. Surprise! It's on sale. Never mind that you haven't had occasion to wear formal attire since your high school prom. This is where it's time to step back and take a look at the life track you are on. Are you or your spouse running for public office? Are you members of the Opera League or up for an Academy Award? Is your cousin Tiffany getting married at the Ritz this fall? If the answer to all these questions is no, forget the dress (unless it's $30 or less … right now I have one of those in my closet).

Doing this may take some backbone. "You deserve it, treat yourself," is one of those unhelpful comments often made by sales associates when they see you mooning over a fabulous and useless item. But before plunking down your precious cash take a moment to assess your life realistically:

- *How do you spend your time?*
- *What is the climate and average temperature where you live?*
- *What are the requirements of your social and work environment?*

When you build a wardrobe around those realities, you are living in the real world and in your own life—and shopping responsibly. Burberry designer Christopher Bailey encourages the 70/30 rule: 70 percent of your clothing should be for practicality, 30 percent for fun.

So what exactly is a lifestyle? It encompasses all we've mentioned above: your climate, the people you share your life with, your personal, professional, and social environments, the activities you put time, energy, and love into. It's reflected in every aspect of your life from the way you decorate your home, cubicle, or locker to the way you spend your free time. Our attire necessarily reflects that lifestyle.

From the style type chart descriptions in Chapter 3 you've probably noticed certain style clusters. I think we gravitate to those places where our intrinsic style is more readily accepted. San Francisco exudes hip Romantic chic, New Yorkers dress up to walk the dog—even if it's just in a designer track suit. Women in Atlanta and Dallas don't wear hats because they wouldn't want to muss up all that wonderful big hair. And in my town, Berkeley, well, anything goes.

[I recently met a woman who described a trip to a tiny little village in Italy. As she was checking into the town's lone hotel, another woman of similar vintage and style walked in, looked her up and down, and asked, "Are you from Berkeley?" They both were and they both embodied the quintessential, Natural Berkeley style. "It's great to live the greatest part of your life in *Whatever*land," she told me. Now, there's a woman who knows and embraces who she is!]

Understanding your lifestyle can become liberating—both to your psyche and to your pocketbook. Whether you're an office executive, a landscape gardener, a schoolteacher, or an engineer, when you shop appropriately for your lifestyle, you will likely find that any new garment or accessory you buy is useful and fits in perfectly with what you already own.

If you consistently buy things that end up sitting in your closet, unworn, here's a little questionnaire you might want to memorize or take with you when you shop. It will help you clarify your lifestyle and determine if something is a keeper:

- ❖ *How much time do I spend at work? What is the dress code there? Will this item work for me in that setting?*

- ❖ *What do I want my clothes to say about me? Does this item help me do that?*

* *Is the fabric warm or cool enough for my home/work/play environment?*

* *Do I have another piece very much like this? How often do I wear it? Could I really use another one just like it? Is it time to replace it?*

* *Where do I spend the most amount of time at home each day? Does this garment suit my needs for the activities I perform at home?*

* *What percent of my time is spent at social engagements? Are they indoors or outdoors? Will this item work for me in my preferred social settings?*

* *How do I spend my recreational/exercise time? Is this item appropriate and necessary for that activity?*

* *Is there a special occasion or trip coming up for which I need a new article of clothing? Will this item suit that occasion?*

If you say yes to any these questions and to the item, it's a good bet you need it and will enjoy wearing it. If you find that you still are attracted to and buy things that don't fit with your lifestyle, maybe you need to ask yourself a different set of questions:

* *Do I like where I live?*

* *Do I like where I work and what I have to wear there?*

* *Am I happy with my friends and my choices of how we spend our nonworking hours?*

* *Do I need to schedule more play or exercise time?*

* *Do I need to develop a lifestyle that better coordinates with what I love to wear?*

* *Do I just need a vacation?*

If you keep choosing attire that is inappropriate for your work environment, your social engagements, or your recreational activities, your subconscious may be trying to tell you something. Pay attention: Take action and you'll eventually transition to a happier and healthier life.

Special Note to Moms

I can just hear the chorus of harried mothers moaning that these questions no longer apply to your life, that thinking about what to wear takes too much time out of your busy day. *Au contraire, mes amies!* It's exactly because you spend your days chasing after toddlers or racing to the market that dressing to feel good about yourself is important. Casual dressing does not have to mean sloppy, drab-colored sweats that won't show spaghetti stains. Even though I wear mostly casual comfortable clothing at my desk, I always make sure I love the colors and that the pieces coordinate well. Wearing my work outfit makes me feel more professional and focused, even if no one is watching.

Making a little extra effort to find active or casual wear in your true colors—and even better, with a shape more flattering than a t-shirt and baggy pants—can really boost your sense of well-being. This is particularly true during child-rearing years, when running errands and taking care of other people is your #1 job and defines your lifestyle. Continuing to play dress-up for the little moments in life keeps us in the game. It also makes a statement to the rest of your family: "I deserve to be seen and appreciated as a whole, beautiful individual and not just as the family go-fer."

How does one do that and keep up a packed family schedule? One of the best ways is to hang entire outfits—active-wear coordinates, pants (or a skirt,) blouse, sweater, and/or jacket—together in your closet. I even have a friend who photographs entire outfits that look good on her so she doesn't have to think about what goes with what. Now *that's* real ready-to-wear.

Ask yourself: *Does this outfit fit my life?*

Shop for Your Size—Now

6

J ackie Gleason, television pioneer and gourmand, had two entire wardrobes for his extreme variations in weight. Most of us have a mini version of this: fat jeans and thin jeans; the sweatpants or sweatshirt that hide a multitude of sins, and a formfitting exercise outfit that shows off our hard work at the gym.

For decades an excessively (and often unhealthy) thin body has been the ideal in the fashion industry. From the point of view of designers, there is a practical reason for this: The more shapeless the human mannequin, the better the garment's cut and drape will show. The designer is not advertising the model; the model is advertising the designer's artistry. Which leads me to the point of this book: Dress to express your inner self—*your* inner artistry. Attempting to be rail thin, if you're not naturally slender, is completely unnecessary. And kind of ridiculous.

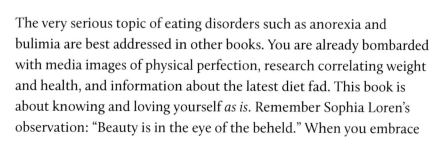

The very serious topic of eating disorders such as anorexia and bulimia are best addressed in other books. You are already bombarded with media images of physical perfection, research correlating weight and health, and information about the latest diet fad. This book is about knowing and loving yourself *as is*. Remember Sophia Loren's observation: "Beauty is in the eye of the beheld." When you embrace who you are right now, you will naturally begin doing things that help you live a happier and healthier life: If that means engaging in more healthful eating habits and exercise routines, all the better.

Having said that, nearly all of us have a little something in the closet—often bought on sale—for which we're just waiting to lose that extra 5 or 10 pounds in order to look smashing. We convince ourselves that the garment is a motivational tool. In reality, every time we see it some part of us feels inadequate. Hanging there unused, charged with judgment, it takes away the value of everything else in our closet that fits and feels comfortable. It is not our friend. It is rarely inspiring. It mocks us.

"Life is too short for uncomfortable shoes," it's been said. I'd paraphrase that: Life is too short for uncomfortable clothes—and for clothes that make you feel awkward or unsure about yourself. Resolve to buy only what makes you feel great today, what complements your figure, and what makes you look confident and happy. Well-fitting clothes send a signal that says, "I know who I am and I like who I am. And you should too!"

If you are serious about dieting and aren't at your ideal weight yet, you can still buy things that don't stretch your pocketbook during the transition period. Here's how: Buy the best and flaunt it—repeatedly. This point was driven home to me when I saw the documentary *September Issue* about *Vogue*'s hefty fall 2009 magazine. The film depicts *Vogue*'s formidable editor in chief, Anna Wintour, coming to the office on different days in the exact same lovely white-and-yellow dress. That woman knows her style and her brand. One of the great secrets of stylish women is that they often buy only a few beautiful pieces at the beginning of a season—sometimes only one suit—and then wear it again and again. They will change a scarf, blouse, sweater, or accessories, but basically, they stick with what works.

As long as you keep your clothing clean and pressed, you don't need the extensive wardrobe of a movie star—or a fashion editor. Having a few high quality, well-cut, flattering clothes is a healthy, sane strategy for anyone's wardrobe and budget, but it makes sense especially when you're going through a period of weight change.

Living With—and Loving—Your Size

Here are some stylists' tips—applicable to anybody, but particularly helpful if you are not yet the size you want to be—that will help you emphasize your best parts:

1) Wear your brightest, most flattering colors near your face. If you don't particularly feel like being that showy then pick one of your eye colors or one of your non-basic colors (maybe something in the purple, green, or orange ranges), and keep the rest of your outfit more neutral.

2) Wearing a single color or tone-on-tone—two shades of the same color—can conceal body points you would rather de-emphasize. It's also, as we said earlier, a very elegant look.

3) Wearing a garment or accessory that ends exactly at your least flattering parts will draw the eye to those areas. If, for example, you don't want to emphasize your derriere, make sure that any blouse, sweater, or jacket—particularly if in a color that contrasts with your skirt or pants—does not end at the widest point there (another reason to have a full-length or even a three-way mirror). This goes for sleeve lengths and accessories, too: The length of a necklace or a shoulder bag will draw the eye to the part of your body where it ends.

   I've noticed a trend among younger women to emphasize their most generous body parts. It seems to be a way of saying, "Yeah, my (fill in the blank) is big, so what?" That's a great personal affirmation. Just make sure to stay within the realm of good taste.

4) Regardless of your size and body shape, make sure the garment fits
well and is cut for your proportions. (These are covered extensively
in Chapters 7 and 8.)

The fit of a garment is essential to making you look chic and feel self-
assured. If the garment is uncomfortable, cut on an awkward bias,
or too tight in any way it can appear ill-fitting. Also, shiny fabrics or
garments that are body-hugging will emphasize the size and shape of
your body.

When you try on a garment, here are some basic questions to ask
yourself about the fit:

* *Is it comfortable?*

* *Do my undergarments show at the armholes or neckline?*

* *Are they obvious under the clothing (e.g., panty line)?*

* *Do I feel confident when I wear this?*

* *Would I want my partner's parents or my boss to see me wearing
  this?*

I added that last one because, as I suggested earlier, some people feel so
confident about their bodies that they're willing to wear something in
public that should really be viewed only in private. It's just something
to think about. As my shopping guide Hella Tsaconas says, when you
get dressed ask yourself: "Where am I going and what do I want to
communicate?"

Undercover Agents

Before we get down to body-type and style-type details, let's literally
start from the inside out. One of the fundamental aspects of dressing
to flatter your size and shape is finding the right undergarments. Back
in the days of seamed boning and densely rubberized fabric it was
something of an insult—psychologically and physically—to wear a

girdle. But with the advent of Spanx, DKNY, and other comfortable body slimmers, hiding or improving your body line becomes a snap.

Whether you want to minimize derriere or thigh jiggle, improve the look of an ample waist, or eliminate love handles, there's something out there for everyone. You might be pleasantly pleased to see how a slimmer may give you a more tailored line—instantly. [Note to you extremely Natural types: If some of your body parts have migrated or expanded their territory, there's nothing wrong with wanting to rein them in with one of these undergarments—particularly for special occasions. The new ones are pretty comfortable.]

Now for me, comfort is crucial in any garment regardless of how yummy or sexy it looks. Nina Garcia, fashion editor for *Marie Claire*, says, "Luxury must be comfortable, otherwise it's not luxury." An ill-fitting bra is not only uncomfortable it can make your clothing look cheap or poorly made. It can also strain your upper back and neck and force you into the stooped posture associated with aging. So before you make any major changes to your wardrobe, go to one of the larger department stores in your area and get a fitting with a bra specialist. (I find this more helpful than rummaging through specialty lingerie stores whose goal is often to help you manufacture more cleavage.) You might be very surprised to discover what your real bra size is.

All the support for your breasts should come from the bra band, not from the straps. If your shoulders have deep strap marks, the straps are too thin. If the bra underwire digs into your ribs you may have the wrong band size. If you're spilling out the top, or there is excess fabric on the sides or top, you have the wrong cup size.

When you shop for undergarments for a specific article of clothing, be sure to bring the garment with you. Make sure the bra or slimmer covers and supports what needs to be covered and supported, while keeping itself hidden from view … unless, of course, you want to show off a lovely piece of lingerie through a sheer blouse. In addition to a couple of comfortable everyday bras, your wardrobe should include at least one T-shirt bra. It will give you a sense of psychological comfort when the outside or indoor temperature changes suddenly from hot to chilly.

A Health Note: Over a lifetime, the way a bra supports your soft tissue—or doesn't—can have an impact on your health. So does the pressure the bra places on your ribs and shoulders. I find the warnings in Sydney Ross Singer and Soma Grismaijer's book *Dressed to Kill* very interesting. The book proposes that very tight underwire bras cut off the body's lymphatic drainage system, keeping toxins stored in the breast tissue and increasing the risk of breast cancer.

There is no scientific proof about about Singer and Grismaijer's claims, but personally, it makes sense to me on a gut level. Having studied various forms of bodywork over the past 30 years I am aware that anything that consistently prevents the free flow of eliminative waste from the body is not a good thing. (That includes non-stretchy jeans you have to shoehorn yourself into.) For that reason I avoid undergarments with stiff, restricting underwires. Fortunately many manufacturers are building bras with more comfortable underwires as well as those without wires these days, even for the well endowed. The better ones tend to be a little pricey, but considering their longevity and quality they're worth it.

Your Body Shape—Accentuate the Positive

Many fashion magazines these days identify four basic body types with illustrative—if not always flattering—names like: Flute, Pear, Apple, and Hourglass. There's an almost oppressive belief that nearly every woman wants to have an hourglass figure (which is why those Diane von Furstenberg's wrap dresses are so flattering—they give every body the shape of an hourglass). But not all of us are built with the broader shoulders, large breasts, tiny waist, and voluptuous hips of a classic hourglass body. My hope is that every woman would want to look healthy and attractive regardless of her body shape or size. So let's look at the concept of dressing a particular body to emphasize *its* best parts.

Knowing the basic shape of your body and learning how to emphasize its best parts can make shopping a lot easier. Several of the fashion magazines these days have taken the lead in this area, illustrating how each body shape can wear some of the newest, fashion-forward styles. The rules are not terribly complicated: emphasize your best features and de-emphasize those that throw your proportions out of balance.

Here is a list of what are considered the basic body shapes:

Pear or dewdrop: smaller through the shoulders—which often slope downward—small waist and larger through the hips.

Apple: larger around the midsection, with either broad or slightly sloping shoulders.

Hourglass: wider shoulders, larger bust, narrow waist, and wider hips.

Rectangle or flute: the typical model's body: narrow hips, of similar size through shoulders, waist, and hips; shoulders may be slightly broader and bust can be small to average.

Working with the following guidelines, it should be fairly easy to pick the most flattering shapes and fabrics to complement your own figure.

When assessing whether a garment is a keeper or a toss, look at yourself in the mirror and ask:

* *What are my best assets?*

* *Does the cut of the cloth, the pattern or detail show them off?*

* *Does this garment deflect the eye from those areas I'd rather not emphasize?*

Again, if you don't want to emphasize a certain part of your body, then just avoid clinging or shiny fabrics, loud patterns, or anything that is tightly fitted across that part. If you want to add something that isn't there, look for garments with structure, detail, pattern, or weave that will help create or add bulk in that area. And always, if you have an asset—your legs, bust, tiny waist, long, lovely neck—*flaunt it.*

Below are some general guidelines to emphasize—or de-emphasize— parts of each basic body shape. If you identify with more than one, try the suggestions for both. Keep in mind that if your style type can't handle ruffles or plunging necklines, you just shouldn't go there.

Pear-shaped: You can create more visual balance by highlighting your upper body. This is easy to achieve with eye-catching necklaces or necklines that have some kind detail, such as ruffles, pleating etc. Also, tops with horizontal emphasis, such as stripes or boat neck t-shirts, will draw the eye upward and balance out your lower body. If you have sloping shoulders you can add some structure to them with tops, jackets, or sweater sets that have traditional inset seams; that means, avoid drape-y, raglan, or kimono-type sleeves. To de-emphasize wide hips go for straight-legged or slightly flared pants rather than skinny ones. A-line skirts or ones that flare softly from the waistline create a more flattering line for you than pencil shapes or anything that hugs the hips and derriere. Jeans with pockets that are high set or close together tend to make the bum appear smaller. Also, anything—dresses, coats or tops—with princess-style shapes or seaming that starts below the bust achieve two goals: drawing the eye to the upper body and away from the hips.

Apple-shaped: Garments with necklines and style lines that feature the upper part of your chest create a portrait for your face and draw the eye away from the waist. These include not-too-deep V-necks, softly draping or sweetheart necklines, large and/or wider collars, and tops with textural details at the shoulder, as well as boat neck tees or tops. Jackets and any top that nips in at the waist visually implies a smaller waistline. Any blouse or or top with an asymmetrical hemline or one that ends at the hipline draws the eye away from a proportionately larger waist. You tend to look best in pants that are straight legged rather than full, as they add a sense of length rather than breadth. Full but not shapeless skirts create a waistline for you, and one that is slightly dropped de-emphasizes a larger waist. (But absolutely avoid low-rise waistbands on both skirts and pants or risk the dreaded muffin top.) Keep in mind that the cleaner you want your waistline to appear, the more unobtrusive—or nonexistent—should be the waistband. Avoid cargo pants entirely—they are very unflattering to an apple-shaped body. Keep your belts thinner rather than wider. Apple shapes often have great legs so don't be afraid to go for shorter hem lengths in your skirts. Mature apple shapes who don't want to go bare or nearly bare-legged can wear shorter lengths with leggings or darker hose.

Hourglass-shaped: You can make the most of your natural assets by emphasizing your bust, hips, and proportionately small waist. For the bust line look for V-neck or surplice tops, fitted shirts with darts, and structured peplum jackets that nip in at the waist. Draping knit fabrics hug your curves and can be very flattering for an hourglass body. A belt or any top that narrows at the waist will emphasize your waistline. If you're short-waisted the belt can hit slightly below your natural waist and should be thin rather than wide. For most average-size hourglass bodies, a slightly flared pant leg (rather than straight or skinny) is flattering, as it follows the wide-narrow-wide shape of your body, but if you're petite and not wearing higher heels, keep the flare narrower so that you don't look shortened and wide. (Most skinny jeans won't fit your proportionately smaller waistline and curvy hips anyway.) Fitted or pencil skirts will highlight your curves, and flared, gathered, or circle skirts emphasize your smaller waist.

Flute-shaped: Flute—or rectangular—body types have the advantage that they can wear multiple styles, shapes, and patterns because they usually aren't trying to distract the eye from any particular body part. Flute shapes can opt for flounces, flares, or anything that creates volume in those areas they'd like to emphasize. For those with shoulders and/or a bust on the shy side, a halter, surplice top or with something in a v-neck, plunging neckline, ruching, or pleating will add some oomph. You're also the type that can easily wear kimono-sleeve tops. Because you tend to be proportionately smaller overall you can wear multiple layers and patterns to add bulk, as well as wide belts and even corsets. Garments with volume around the hips and derriere—created by either structure like ruching at the hipline or a bold pattern—can create visual curves. You're the one body type that can successfully wear pants with a high waist (they used to call them a Hollywood waist) or those with inverted pleats (especially nice on those with small hips and thinner legs), as well as slightly flared leg and (yes!) skinny jeans. Jeans with pockets set low or wide on the rear add a sense of breadth to your derriere. You can also wear pleated skirts and those that create fullness around hips with gathers, flounces, tiers, and dirndl or tulip shapes.

There's also a reverse variation on the pear shape called the **Inverted Triangle**, characterized by broad shoulders and narrow hips. If that describes your body, follow the guidelines for the hourglass figure with these additions: You can draw attention away from your shoulders and toward the center line of your body with V-necks, halter tops, and asymmetrical necklines. Look for details at the hip line that add volume, such as pockets, gathering, or pleats. Shorter skirts and eye-catching shoes that make a real fashion statement will draw attention to your legs.

And here are just a few more basic proportion rules for everyone to keep in mind. Wearing a belt or garment with a waistline that sits slightly below your natural waist will lengthen your torso; a shortened or higher waistline will shorten your torso. Plain pumps make the legs look longer; ankle straps, Mary Jane straps and laces make legs look shorter. Wearing a single color elongates the line of the body. (We'll go over some of this in more detail in chapter 8.)

A Note About Sizing

Clothing sizes can be deceiving. When I cleaned out my closet this year (an annual event) I tried on my quite aged, much-loved, winter-white silk blouse and decided to give it away. Suddenly, I practically swam in it. The size read 2.

It's not an uncommon experience to discover that last year's size 8 is this year's 6. Perhaps designers size apparel smaller so that you will feel better about a garment—and yourself—and buy it. Maybe there is a powerful cabal in Paris or Milan that decides that sizes will read smaller or larger this year. We'll never know. The fact is that sizes vary according to designer, and sometimes from year to year. As you progress on your path to closet enlightenment, just make sure that you always have something that you feel great in regardless of the number on the label.

And here's a little food for thought: the most popular wedding dress size in the US these days ... is a size 14.

Ask yourself: *Does it fit and does it flatter?*

Make New Friends

7

By this point you have learned that unless you (A) are a professional stylist, (B) have impeccable natural taste, or (C) have really done your homework, you need some help shopping for the real you.

Here's why. No matter how expert we are about our color and style, sometimes we just don't clearly see how we look in a particular garment. Perhaps we're attached to an old favorite we wore when we were younger or at a different weight. It even happens to people in the limelight. I watched a very famous author give a keynote address wearing a suit that revealed, through the jacket, some rather ample love handles. Her jacket ached at the buttonholes and seams. The skirt disclosed a well-fed tummy and generous derriere. A women in the audience near me turned to a neighbor and whispered, "Doesn't she have a friend who could help her dress?"

A friend like that is one of the greatest gifts we can have: someone who knows and loves us enough to be honest and objective and wants us to look our best. If you don't have such a friend, get a three-way mirror. (A good full-length mirror is important for everyone.) Better yet, gather a team of trusted companions to work with.

Here's how I began cultivating my team. In my fashion-phobic days, preparing for an even mildly dressy occasion was a challenge. I would stare into my closet until I became glassy-eyed, finally pulling together the safest, most boring neutral-colored outfit I could find. On one such occasion, an afternoon lunch with friends, I sat across the table from an acquaintance, Margaret, one of the most quintessentially chic women in our circle of women. I found myself staring at her, riveted by her appearance. Clearly she noticed but was too polite to ask, "Do you have a problem?" At the end of the lunch, I ran up to her and said, "I'd love to go shopping with you someday. I need to learn how to accessorize!"

After we both stopped laughing, we did make that shopping date, one that started a 25-year friendship and helped set me on the path to fashion fulfillment. Throughout the years I've learned a lot from Margaret about what looks flattering on me, how to shop wisely, and about life in general. With gratitude for her deep friendship and wisdom, I'd like to share one of Margaret's key shopping rules:

Find the designers and companies that cut for your body and style, and stay with them.

Fashion designer Gareth Morris, who has worked for couture houses and mass merchandisers, explains: "Fit is the one thing you can generally count on year after year from a particular design house."

Once you know which designers work for you, shopping outlet malls and sale racks can be a pleasure instead of a headache-inducing waste of time and money. "I always come back to a few designers whose clothing consistently works for me," Margaret says.

During one of our treks to a favorite outlet mall, I left Margaret at the Ellen Tracy store and trudged through at least six other shops. Two hours later, after I'd gone through rack after rack trying dozens of things, I reconnected with her. She had also tried on dozens of things but picked out exactly *two* items. Patience is one of the greatest shopping virtues, as she demonstrated. You may spend all day shopping and find nothing that works—and that's OK. But when you do find an item that works, or that can be made to work, it's a revelation and a thing of beauty. And those two items Margaret selected looked great on her. "This is my style," she said about Ellen Tracy. "I know I will find something here that fits and that coordinates with what I already have"—including the Ellen Tracy pieces she'd bought in previous seasons.

Another of Margaret's shopping secrets: She always pays cash for her clothing. She budgets carefully for her wardrobe, so she is very purposeful about what she buys. Shopping with cash requires more thought than just whipping out a credit card. It's a good strategy, especially during economically challenging times. (Full disclosure: I rarely do.)

So Margaret taught me about two friendships: the one of an honest, loving comrade-in-shopping who will candidly tell you how you look in something, and the other, a design house that will design for your frame and style year after year.

A major plus of staying with designers who cut for your body is that their clothes are not likely to cost you a lot in alterations.

Tinker, Tailor ...

Having said that, nearly everyone needs a good tailor. I used to be amazed to see starlets who were no taller than I (5'1" on a good day) wearing red-carpet-ready gowns that fit them perfectly. I can't even buy a good pair of jeans that fit quite right. Then I learned that behind every well-heeled s a well-trained tailor. As designer Michael Kors says, "There's no such thing as *ready-to-wear*." Truly well-dressed women and men nearly always have their clothes altered. The extra cost of hemming, letting out, taking in, removing bulky or unnecessary belt loops, or even changing buttons will make the garment your own. You will feel happy and, more important, comfortable every time you wear it.

In truth, it's the rare person who is a perfect size 4 or 8, or 16. To be profitable, clothing designers must design for a common denominator. Even the most diligent shopper, working with a skilled stylist and sticking with her preferred designers, will find that a close-to-perfect garment may still need a little tweaking. Just about all of the higher end department stores offer alterations free of charge; in lower-tier stores, alterations are usually available for what your local tailor charges.

As recently as 20 years ago quality construction was for those who could afford higher-end garments. But many of today's top designers produce well-made items, sometimes from natural fibers, for companies like Kohl's, Kmart, JCPenney, and Target. What makes these downscale pieces work is, of course, perfect fit. I've paid $30 for alterations on a $50 Target wool coat that lasted multiple seasons. So there's no reason you can't look chic and up-to-date without having to replace your entire wardrobe every year.

There's an assumption that if you can afford to have your clothes custom made, you'll get the best fit. That's true, of course, especially if you also have a great tailor, a great body, and the time. However, a seamstress or tailor can also fit you *too* perfectly, accentuating parts you'd rather not have accentuated. Finding an item off the rack that looks 90 percent terrific and then having it altered only slightly may be better than having it emphasize undesirable curves, a broad derriere, or a short waist.

One of my favorite new websites is called Fashion Fit Formula (www.fashionfitformula.com) developed by Janet Wood and Kathy McFadden. Their system will identify the exact points on your body, based on your precise measurements, that are most flattering for hemlines, sleeve lengths, necklaces, etc. Just be VERY precise when you take your measurements to fill out the form on their site. You'll receive a list (in inches or millimeters) indicating exactly where to alter your hemlines, sleeves, etc. Print it out, show it to your tailor or seamstress, and you'll be able to transform almost any garment from dumpy to chic.

Your FASHION FIT FORMULA Solution Provides You With Your Best Look

Visit www.fashionfitformula.com **to get started.**
When you apply your unique measurements to your clothing you will immediately look taller, thinner and more polished.

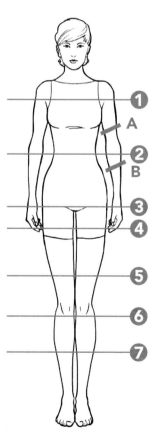

1) Optimal Neckline or Necklace

A, B) Short and 3/4 Length Sleeves

2) Cropped Jacket, Waist with Belt

3) Leg/Torso Length Jacket or Outside Shirt, Sweater

4) Standard or Blazer Length Jacket, Micro-Mini Skirt, Short Shorts

5) 3/4 Length Jacket, Mini–Skirt, Bermuda Shorts

6) Street Length Skirt, Dress, Coat or Short Capris

7) Mid-Calf Length Skirt, Long Capris and Coat Length

One note about alterations: Knit items like sweaters and dresses are particularly difficult to find in the right proportions for everyone's body. I can't think of any alteration that will make a badly proportioned sweater fit. So if it's just a little too long or short but the color, style, and texture are absolutely perfect for you—and you love it—go ahead. Belt it. Accessorize it. Wear it with aplomb. If it's a knit fabric in a suit, however, you'd be amazed at what a tailor can do. I've seen garments with very little seam width let out and stitched back beautifully.

Are You Being Served?

If you're doing serious shopping at higher-end department stores or boutiques, "friendship" is part of the deal. Neiman Marcus, Saks Fifth Avenue, Nordstrom, Lord & Taylor, Henri Bendel, Bergdorf Goodman, Bloomingdale's, Barney's, and even Macy's have personal shoppers or trained sales personnel who work with customers to help them find designers best suited for their body type and to navigate the look *du jour*. We can be thankful this trend is moving into several of the smaller chain clothing stores; they are now also providing in-store personal stylists trained to understand how their clothing works for different body types and styles.

A Nordstrom stylist explained to me that depending on this year's silhouette even your favorite designer's slacks may not flatter you. For example, if slacks are featuring pleated fronts and you look best in flat, a personal shopper can eliminate items that won't work for your body type.

Of course department store mannequins have been outfitted head-to-toe by some of the best stylists around: You could always simply purchase the entire package as shown on the mannequin, assuming it suits your coloring and style. But whether you're shopping with a store stylist or online, be alert: Have your color swatches in hand and your style types clear in your mind. And don't be swayed by others when your gut says "no."

On the shopping team you've assembled, a personal shopper trained in color and style analysis can end up being your best friend. If you have the time and resources to work with one, you'll find it a very worthwhile investment. My friend Hella Tsaconas, an artist trained by John Kitchener at Personal Style Counselors, has been a godsend to me and many of my friends. Every season she checks out the merchandise available in the department stores and boutiques. She can even map out a strategy for her clients' shopping day before they ever set foot inside a store. Personal shoppers are particularly helpful for professionals who are putting together a work-appropriate wardrobe or an ensemble for a special event. They can also go through your closet periodically to suggest ways of putting pieces together or help you eliminate those that no longer work for you.

Another new friend to cultivate: a knowledgeable salesperson. My dear friend Jan, an investment advisor, developed a great working relationship with one of the saleswomen at her favorite department store. The woman understood Jan's coloring and style and always called her when items from her favorite designers came in stock. What's more, she also phoned Jan when they were about to go on sale— sometimes actually holding them for her a day before the sale started! A good sales associate will willingly go the extra mile to make sure you get your money's worth. It's great to have someone like that on your team, particularly when you're shopping for what we like to call "investments"—pricier pieces you expect to last many seasons.

And there's one other friend who can help you shop: a total stranger. When you happen upon someone whose size, style, and/or coloring seems very similar to your own, don't be afraid to ask them where they shop. Most people will feel flattered and can be a tremendous resource for locating designers and boutiques you may not have known about.

A Note about Online Shopping

The online shopping experience has been vastly improved lately with the addition of customer reviews. When you click on a particular garment you'll find a link to comments by shoppers who have already ordered the item you are looking at. From these you'll learn things such as "order up one size" or "fabric was more see-through than I am used to wearing" or "not the color shown in the picture." Many times these reviewers also include their age, body shape, and dress size. That information is extremely helpful for determining whether a garment might work for you. It can also help you avoid the cost of sending back things that didn't work.

In summary:

- ✤ *Favor designers who design for your body*
- ✤ *Find a good tailor*
- ✤ *Work with professionals*
- ✤ *Make friends with a good salesperson*
- ✤ *Talk—and listen—to strangers*

Ask Yourself: *Is my team helping reveal the real me?*

The Physics and Mathematics of Shopping: Proportion, Balance, and Scale

8

M athematics? *Physics*??? Don't worry, you math- and science-phobes. We're just trying to help you create an image that makes sense in terms of your size and stature.

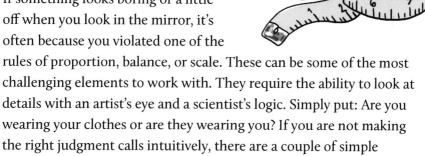

If something looks boring or a little off when you look in the mirror, it's often because you violated one of the rules of proportion, balance, or scale. These can be some of the most challenging elements to work with. They require the ability to look at details with an artist's eye and a scientist's logic. Simply put: Are you wearing your clothes or are they wearing you? If you are not making the right judgment calls intuitively, there are a couple of simple formulas, applicable to all style types that can often help make the process easier.

Proportion: Don't Harm the Harmony

Proportional harmony requires a bit of mathematical thinking when you pair what you are wearing on the upper half of your body with what are you wearing on the bottom. Here's how it works: Anyone who ever took a figure drawing class will remember that the so-called average body consists of eight head lengths: one length for the head, two from the neck to the waist, one from the waist to the hip, two from the hip to the knee, and two from knee to heel.

I know this doesn't apply perfectly to many of us (my short waist attests to that) but the point is this: When you use garments, colors, or patterns to divide your body in half—without any other breaks in the line, you usually create a dumpy image, one with a sense of stagnation. This is particularly true if the upper and lower garments are of the same width.

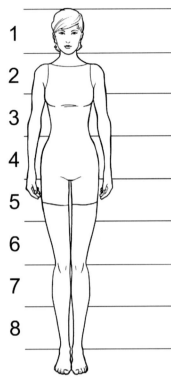

The human psyche gravitates toward things that imply motion, so you want your

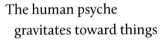

clothing to be in conversation rather than at a standoff. Think about it in terms of music. A marching band playing music in 4/4 time can be very inspiring, but the effect is not very sexy. Syncopation—a rhythm that's a little offbeat, that holds you and then lets you go—engages your entire being and makes you want to move. That's why we want to use color or cut in a way that draws the eye from one area to another in a graceful manner.

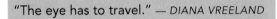

"The eye has to travel." — DIANA VREELAND

Here are some examples to demonstrate the concept of proportional harmony that keeps the eye moving. Don't get too hung up on the math, just think about the general idea.

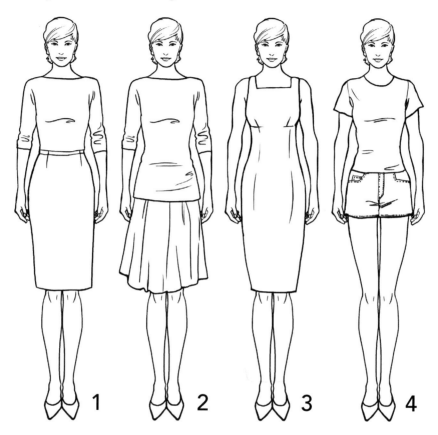

In figure 1 the blouse comes to the waist (two head lengths from shoulder to waist) and the skirt comes to the knees (three, from waist to knees), creating a ratio between the blouse and the skirt of 2:3. That leaves three lengths uncovered—the head and lower legs. Figure 2 shows the same proportions in reverse order: three lengths on the top, two on the skirt.

In figure 3 the sheath has a total of five head lengths from shoulder to knee. The face and lower legs make up the other three lengths, creating the ratio of 5:3.

In figure 4 the T-shirt covers two head lengths, the shorts one, for a ratio of 2:1. Together, they make for a total of three head lengths covered, five uncovered (head and upper and lower legs), or 3:5.

Are you seeing a pattern here? These are the ratios (and their reverse) that keep the eye moving: 1:2, 2:3, and 3:5. What you won't find are ratios of 2:4 or 4:4. Now what is fascinating about these numbers is that they are the beginning of what is called Fibonacci's ratio. This formula is found throughout nature and has been used in many disciplines from architecture to advertising because it speaks to us on a very primal level. It delineates the structural elegance of a nautilus shell, the unfolding petals on a rose, and the spiral pattern of a galaxy. How fitting then, that these same proportions can also apply to our clothing!

There are multiple ways you can create these ratios to establish proportional harmony. You can establish division points with garments of different colors, patterns, a pattern and a solid, by adding a belt or by adding a jacket with a nipped-in waistline. All of these will create breaks in the visual line to keep the eye moving.

So let's apply this principle to fix the dumpy 4:4 ratio outfit shown earlier. We'll shorten the jacket and define a break at the waist, thereby creating three lengths from shoulders to hips and five from waist to ankle. We will also narrow the sleeves and pants bottoms to eliminate the overall boxy feel of the first version.

Now here's the kicker. Few of us are divided up neatly into eight even head lengths. Some of us have disproportionately long legs (not that that's a problem!) or short waists, or are long from the waist to the hip, etc. Even sleeves can impact proportional balance: They can appear either three-quarter or wrist length, depending on the length of one's arms. So what's a person to do to look more balanced? Either have a terrific seamstress with an impeccable eye for proportion or, as mentioned in the last chapter, check out the Fashion Fit Formula (www.fashionfitformula.com). They'll provide you with a PDF showing exactly where to alter your clothes for *your* body. It's a great help in achieving the most proportionally pleasing, body-flattering hemline, sleeve length, etc.

Now, there are other challenges to this formula too, based on current fashion trends. Not that long ago, just about every garment could be altered or adjusted to conform to these ratios. These days, many designers intentionally create pieces that straddle these division points or break the head-length rule entirely. Or they create individual pieces that are balanced in relation to each other but not necessarily to the body wearing them. Asymmetrical shapes and hemlines present their own problems. Depending on who is wearing any of these garments, the effect can be striking, lovely—or dissonant.

But for traditional classic pieces—dresses, skirts, jackets, blouses, sweaters, pants, suits—as long as the garments' delineation points conform to the basic ratios (1:2, 2:3, 3:5), at least when seen from the front, you'll achieve the effect of visual balance.

After a while, seeing the right division points will just become second nature—you won't have to obsess on this rule or carry around a measuring tape with you. If something works for your body you'll know it.

Balancing Act

Avoid top or bottom loading! You can certainly wear something like an a-line or tunic-style top with wide-legged palazzo pants, particularly if you're wearing footwear that elongates your legs. But if you're wearing a much wider-cut garment on one part of your body, you'll look more balanced if what you wear on the other part is cut more narrowly. Here's an example: You can pair a pencil skirt, straight pants, or leggings with a looser, boxier, or more flowing jacket, blouse, or tunic. Conversely, if you're wearing a billowy skirt or boot-cut pants, you'll look more balanced wearing something more fitted on top, like a body-hugging jacket, T-shirt, or sweater. You can certainly wear a looser or draped outer garment, as long as the one closest to the body is more fitted.

Here's how my shopping guru, Hella Tsaconas, visually summarizes this rule:

Also make sure that your footwear grounds you proportionately. For example, if you're wearing a larger piece like a wool swing coat (assuming your style and height can carry it off) a boot or a sturdy pump will anchor you more than a sling-back kitten heel or a pair of ballet flats. (OK—Audrey Hepburn could get away with it, and I suppose you could too if you had her height and overall style types.) This is especially important for shorter women, as wearing anything too large on the top of the body will visually weigh them down. Likewise, if you're wearing Ugg boots you'd want to wear something bulkier on top than a flowing chiffon blouse. Yes, it's sometimes *fashionable* to wear a chiffon blouse with Ugg boots ... but let's get real, ladies: If it's cold enough to wear Uggs, do you really want to wear a sheer blouse? And, if it's hot enough for a sheer blouse, who wants to schlep around in sweaty Uggs?

Scale

Another important aspect of proportional dressing is achieving the right scale. Almost any edgy or fashion-forward element can be adopted if the scale is appropriate for the wearer. Appropriate scale means that the pattern, accessory, buttons, ribbing, or trim features, and amount of fabric or cut are in proportion to your body size. Those of us with bodies outside the average height or size range battle with this issue all the time. (It's a large part of why I got interested in the subject of personal style in the first place.)

When it comes to scale, something oversize or shrunken can be charming or silly, depending on who is wearing it. Most stylists feel that oversize garments are for tall or large people and undersize ones are for the petite. That's a good general rule, but it's not always true. A petite person with a lot of bounce in her personal style can carry off something a bit oversize, too, like the boyfriend jacket that appears every 10 years or so. That's also true for an item like a hooded winter poncho.

The point is, if your style can support a more theatrical-looking garment just make sure you aren't *swimming* in it. A boyfriend jacket shouldn't fall just above your kneecaps, nor should the bottom of the armholes hit at your waistline. (Remember the head-count ratio rule.) When you wear clothes that are *unintentionally* over- or undersize you can end up looking as though you're wearing hand-me-downs. Make the effort to have those items altered, if possible, so that they fit your proportions.

By now you've learned that if you are tall—whether a willowy Angelic type or a Dramatic femme fatale—you can probably get away with more fabric and larger accessories (belts, purses, scarves, and jewelry). A taller woman whose personality leans more toward goddess will find that wearing something too tiny, fitted, or shrunken (particularly in vests or jackets) creates dissonance. And no amount of tailoring, hemming, or button-changing is going to make a dramatic, oversize garment appropriate for a very small person, no matter how perfect its color or pattern.

Patterns

High fashion is the sizzle that sells magazines and nowhere is this
more evident than in some of the wilder patterns shown on the
Fashion Week runways. Some designers create pieces that are more
accurately described as works of wearable art than as clothing intended
to flatter the human body. This is why they hire tall überthin human
"mannequins" to show off their designs. Those tall elegant creatures
are far less likely to look ridiculous in a large or dramatic pattern or
exaggerated cut. (Although some models are starting to look pretty silly
as a few designers seem to have thrown out all pretense of trying to
design for a woman's body.) Because of this, when I peruse high fashion
magazines I simply consider them as inspirational tools—art books—
rather than indicators of what I should be wearing this season.

Of course, by the time this year's hot design or pattern makes its way
to your local department store it will have been adapted for the general
population. Still, translating that look to our own individual style

and size is an art in itself. When
you're flipping through the glossy
pages of a catalogue and come
across a beautiful pattern, be
sure to use a critical eye. See
something you like? Does
it complement your style,
your coloring and your
size? If so, then by all
means go ahead and buy it.

For example, if you love stripes and
stripes are in this year, wear them
but pay attention to what kind of
stripes they are. Are you plus-sized
or petite? It goes without saying that

large, wide horizontal stripes can make you look even larger and be out of proportion to someone of small stature. You could end up looking like a bumble bee. (Somewhere there's a picture of me doing just that. I think it was featured in the *DON'T* section of a magazine.) Another note about stripes and color: if you have more blended coloring with less contrast between your hair, eyes and skin tones, pick stripes that blend in tone rather than bounce off each other.

The matching rule applies to other patterns, too. Does the pattern compete with you for attention? Or does it enhance your intrinsic coloring and style? For an Angelic type or a delicately boned person, regardless of size, large color blocks or bold patterns can be overwhelming. Likewise a tiny, delicate pattern, even if in the right colors, can make a dramatic type look silly.

Textural patterns such as the thickness of the wale in corduroy or the ribbing on a sweater also matter. A finely boned or smaller person would appear more balanced in fine-wale rather than thicker corduroy, and smaller knit ribs rather than wider. Someone with more dramatic style or more height can carry off wider wale corduroy and chunkier knits. The size of the ribbing on a sweater trim should also be in proportion to your height and size.

You can certainly throw out some of the ancient conventional wisdom such as, don't mix prints. The key is to pay attention to the *scale* of the prints. Make sure the patterns, texture, and weave—and accessories—complement rather than overwhelm each other. They should also be in the same color temperature. Just be sure that the overall look doesn't appear too studied. You never want to look like you're trying too hard. Things that work have an effortless ease; things that are overdone project desperation. If you've got too much going on, like multiple patterns, lots of eye-catching accessories and colors, remember Coco Chanel's dictum: Always remove one accessory. Apply that idea to patterns and colors as well. You'll likely end up with a better look.

Accessories

Scale is very important in everything from bags to belts, shoes, jewelry, and even eyeglasses. An accessory of awkward size can throw off an outfit that is otherwise perfect.

Shoes: Shoes deserve their own encyclopedia, so I'll just touch briefly on the subject. So many rules have been broken lately about what kind of shoe goes with what skirt length or pant shape that I hesitate to set any hard-and-fast guidelines here. In general, the more casual you intend to look, regardless of what else you're wearing, the more you will look balanced by wearing flats or something with a smaller heel. The more edgy, sexy, or formal the rest of your attire, the more you can wear a higher heel. Just always keep proportion in mind. Stratospheric stiletto heels on us shorties can come off as desperate or tart-y.

And, it must be said, comfort first. If you intend to buy a pair of heels, especially pricey ones, make absolutely sure they're going to be comfortable in the long run. Wear them for an extended period around the house, preferably on carpet, before wearing them for an event. If anything about them is causing you grief—take them back. And if you're at a more formal event, you might want to carry a pair of those fold-up shoes in gold or silver to slip on when your feet start screaming. (Thankfully designers are showing beautiful shoes with lower heels this year. We'll see how long that trend lasts.)

Most wardrobe consultants feel that it's a good idea for nearly everyone to have a pair of skin-colored shoes in her wardrobe. They appear to melt into your legs, making them look longer. That can be very sexy, and helpful if you're short but also if your feet are particularly large. But be careful: Go a shade lighter or brighter than your skin tone and your shoes can say, "Hey! Look at my big feet!" Generally, you don't want to call attention to your footwear if it comes at the expense of the rest of your look—unless you're young, of course, and/or want to show off shapely, toned legs. If your personal style and size can carry off something more edgy, then let your shoes make a statement—but only to the extent that they remain in proportion to the rest of your ensemble.

Belts: Someone with a short waist should be careful about the width of a belt. If wide belts are in and you're tiny, make sure the width of the belt doesn't eclipse your entire torso and cut into your bust line. This can shift the proportion ratios out of whack. If you have a medium to long rise, you can also wear a belt (or pant waistline) that sits below your natural waist and it will bring the rest of your body into a more balanced proportion. Someone with a very classic style type, regardless of size, can usually go with a narrow or medium width belt. Taller, bold, romantic, or bohemian-type casuals can get away with larger-scale belts with more embellishment.

Jewelry: A fun, often less-expensive way to be fashion-forward each season is with a new piece of jewelry. If chunky, bold jewelry is popular you can certainly wear a statement piece—as long as it's scaled appropriately to your size and doesn't compete with a garment neckline. Taller, larger, or more expressively dramatic types can carry off more heft and dazzle. If you're wearing a piece over bare skin, very tiny delicate jewelry tends to work best on younger necks and bust lines or on those with finer skin texture and features. If the piece rests on top of a garment, you can wear any kind of delicate jewelry as long as it is in line with your style type(s). Big hair hides tiny earrings. Also, remember that jewelry, like hemlines, calls attention to the part of the body where it rests. Emphasize only those areas that you feel comfortable showing off. (The Fashion Fit Formula website can also help you choose the right length of a necklace or earrings.)

As mentioned in the style chapter, matching the predominant shape of your face with that of your jewelry creates a nice emphasis for your primary style facets. Round shapes in earrings, beads, and gemstones complement rounder facial features. For those with a square, triangular, or rectangular shaped face, design shapes that feature some angularity help create a pleasing visual harmony in your overall look. And if you're clearly an oval, look for elongated, oval, or teardrop designs.

Handbags: For better or worse, oversize handbags will always be in style. They give designers a chance to be wildly creative. If you're over 5'7" you can probably carry off an enormous handbag that looks like luggage women schlepped onto the Orient Express in the 1930s. If you're under 5'5", however, that same bag can make you look like you're about to topple over. A very large bag might also make you look thin by contrast, but mostly it's going to look like your burden. Likewise, too little a bag on a very tall person can just get lost, unless it's something like a beaded or crystal clutch for a formal event.

One theory says that your handbag should be no wider than your body. That's a little impractical, but generally, the more heft you have, regardless of height, the larger the bag you can get away with. Still, a bag large enough for a weekend adventure is not appropriate for everyday use. Besides, oversized handbags—and the people who carry them—get scrutinized very carefully by store security. And honestly, ladies, those enormous handbags will eventually create posture issues. For every body type. Our bodies were just not built to carry large, stuff-laden satchels slung over our shoulders. (I know—women in developing countries balance large, heavy baskets on top of their heads, walking with perfect alignment and grace. That's not the same as slinging an enormous handbag over one shoulder.) You may not care about this too much when you're younger, but trust me, as you age those heavy bags—just like those sexy stilettos—take their toll.

If you need a really large bag to carry around all your stuff, it may be time to reconsider just how much stuff it's essential to have with you at all times. If you have to carry more than your purse will hold, then you probably need some kind of briefcase or tote. Tote bags have become a standard fashion accessory and come in a variety of sizes as well as a wide range of styles from the sophisticated to the utilitarian.

To conclude, think of yourself as a product of nature or a work of art. Begin to develop an eye for balance by asking: Does what I am wearing create a sense of balance and harmony? The goal is to create an image that makes the viewer say *ahhh* rather than *ha ha*.

Let's review these principles of balance, scale, and proportion. Keep them in mind when you look at yourself in the mirror:

❖ *Think odd—1:2, 2:3, and 3:5—rather than even—4:4. Don't cut yourself in half.*

❖ *Anchor yourself with equal (visual) weight on both ends of your body.*

❖ *Balance bigger or flowy garments on one end with fitted and tailored on the other.*

❖ *Wear your clothes—don't swim in them. And don't be restricted by them.*

❖ *Choose patterns, fabric textures, and garment details scaled for your height and size.*

❖ *Wear your accessories. Don't let them wear you.*

See, it's really not that hard. Just think like a scientist—or an artist!

Ask yourself: *Am I expressing my true essence—in a balanced way?*

Polishing the Stone

9

My assumption is that you've read through this whole book first before trying to implement these rules. Again, change is most effective when it's made with awareness and patience, so here are some basic principles to help you get started with that change. Many of them are so well-known as to almost be cliché. But truth is never a cliché.

Let's start on the inside. Regardless of what you do with your wardrobe, if you are not living a healthful life, if you are not happy on the inside, you will not project beauty, grace, and authenticity. My own path to inner peace (something I share with Oprah and Dr. Oz by the way!) is paved by the Transcendental Meditation® program, which I have practiced for more than 45 years.

Wearing the right clothes in your colors should simply be the icing on the cake for your inner development. In my own experience, they've always seemed to go hand in hand. The more comfortable I feel in my own skin, the more I choose the right things to wear.

Now, for the outer expressions of that inner development: These are for your own benefit, first and foremost, because they are affirmations of the way you feel about yourself.

Cleanliness

It doesn't matter whether you're a buttoned-down CEO or a dreadlocked rocker—keep it clean. With the exception of our canine companions, most beings we interact with are attracted to those who

135

are well-groomed, neat, and clean. Well-kept hair, body, and nails are affirmations of the respect you have for yourself and those in your environment. Wearing clean, well-pressed clothing tells the world (and potential employers, friends or life partners) that you pay attention, notice details, and hold them in great enough esteem to put some effort into making a good first impression—or second or tenth one.

You'll earn more respect and gain more influence with a few well-kept pieces than a never-ending carousel of trendy looks. Visit the cleaners or the Laundromat as often as necessary. *Never* wear stained clothing.

Quality

Part of becoming a butterfly is seeing yourself as beautiful during the transition into your true self. So there's real value in keeping one or two long-lasting, well-made pieces with you for the duration. As we covered in the chapter on stylishness, a beautifully tailored trench coat or suede jacket, a simple, elegant dress, beautiful slacks, or a cashmere sweater—these kinds of wardrobe cornerstones give you the versatility to go from casual to dressy. You can always take them fashion-forward with a few trendy or less expensive pieces like fun costume jewelry or T-shirts in your best colors.

Savvy shoppers know you don't need to spend a fortune on the best (that's why God created the outlet mall and high-end vintage clothing stores). Once you have your colors and style down, you will more likely find things at those stores that flatter you. However, do yourself a big favor: Don't make the sale rack your first stop. If something is on the sale rack or at an outlet mall, it's often there for good reason. (When a fad or trend has just about run out of steam you'll often see it on sale everywhere and in exaggerated form, e.g., excessive studs, bedazzling, crazier color combinations and patterns.) See what's out there that makes you look and feel fabulous. Then, if the latest thing is beyond your budget, check to see what's on sale that may be similar. Just be sure the sale item is also a quality piece that fits well or can be tailored to do so.

Affluence

Years ago there was an article in *Town & Country* magazine that ran down the principles of making a home look affluent and refined. If you did just two things, the piece said, you could achieve the look of elegance: Lay out the money for expensive picture framing and good Persian carpets. I would say dressing well follows a similar rule. If you splurge on only two things make them the things people see framing your face and anchoring you to the ground: your hair and your shoes. (Anthony Cabrera, the author of *101 Things I Learned in Design School*, writes: "Your shoes say who you are; your hair says how you want to be perceived.") Well-cut, healthy hair will make any outfit look better and will make you feel good inside. Well-made beautiful shoes will do the same. More important, they will likely be comfortable which can definitely show on the outside.

Simplicity

Wild hair and vampire eyes are for the runway or the stage, not the office...unless you work in a tattoo parlor. Even someone with a very dramatic style can command more appreciative attention by limiting the boldness they express through attire and makeup. [Trust me, you bolder types—you'll get noticed on the basis of your personality alone!] This is particularly true today in our relentlessly in-your-face culture. Less is more.

The reason simplicity in dressing is a virtue is that complexity requires too much thinking. You never want to look as though you have over thought what you're wearing. We're talking about clothes here after all, not your whole life. You want to make your clothing choices as easy as possible so you can get on with what your life is really about—work, friends, family, spiritual values, and personal growth.

Stand Up for Yourself!

Literally. This seems like such a simple thing, but it's hard for some of us because it requires the willingness to become visible. Our bodies telegraph so clearly what is going on in our hearts and our minds. This is especially true as we age: The slouch associated with aging tells the world, "I've given up." When you stand up straight—not throwing back your shoulders or thrusting out your chest but being grounded on your heels and balanced so that your spine and the long bones of your legs support your body—you tell the world, and more important, yourself, "I deserve to be seen."

If you have long-held damaging beliefs about yourself, you'll likely have long-established postural imbalances to overcome. If that's the case, get thee to a personal trainer, stat! Or, better yet, start working with a very knowledgeable body worker who understands how to help you change your muscular patterns to reestablish where your vertebrae should be. This can gradually change some emotional patterns as well. Correct posture will not only make you look more vital, it will also take pressure off your internal organs and help them move more freely.

Be willing to become visible, breathe and take up the space you deserve.

Ask yourself: *Is my image polished and refined?*

Let's Begin

10

You'll notice that we waited to the last chapter to say, "Let's Begin." It's tempting to want to jump in and implement these ideas immediately. But being comfortable with the fundamentals of color and style is just the starting point. It takes some time to imbibe these principles and to use them intelligently.

So allow yourself to "date" your colors and style for a while before making major changes to your wardrobe. If you decide to work with a stylist be sure to do your homework so that you find someone with good references who is willing to work with these principles too.

Simplify

I'm a big fan of ease and comfort (typical for someone with a lot of the Natural style). I'd prefer not to have to think too much or work too hard when I get dressed. For that reason I group my clothes by color and type (pants, blouses, T-shirts, sweaters, jackets, etc). I find that having things visually laid out within my color palette is both pleasing and helps me choose what goes with what. But I also like to hang entire outfits together because I'm all for uniforms. Some style archetypes abhor this concept but when I say uniform, I mean *your* uniform: what works for you and is repeatable.

Another great idea is to have a friend photograph you in some of your favorite looks (or take pictures of yourself—and don't forget shoes and accessories). Keep the pictures in a file on your smart phone or printed out in a binder in your closet. This is a fun exercise and will help you train your eye to see what works. It also shows up the gaps in your wardrobe so that you can shop purposefully, rather than go only for whatever is new and attention grabbing. My dear friend Judy LaMar, fine artist and stylist extraordinaire, once went through my closet with me and put together several combinations of my clothes, many of which I never would have imagined. She then made up a list of what I needed and which pieces any new item would work with. Nothing beats an expert's eye.

All this can remove the panicky, haphazard pattern of grabbing whatever happens to be clean and convenient and replaces it with effortless and foolproof dressing. It makes your life calmer. It also saves oodles of time and aggravation, especially on days when for hormonal or other reasons you just don't feel great. Knowing you are put together and well dressed removes a key hurdle when your day seems filled with them.

Purging and Honing, or Breaking Up is Hard to Do

Even timeless, classic pieces can become dated. Sometimes you can get a second life out of those garments with some minor alterations. Something as simple as taking up a hem can bring a garment up to date. This is particularly the case with outerwear. However, sometimes we can hold onto something too long. When I do, I remember some of my favorite thoughts from Karl Lagerfeld; he said that the past makes the present secondhand and, if the past was better, you might as well give up; you must adapt to changing times; notions, concepts, and visions change. This is the charm and the allure of fashion. It keeps us moving forward in life.

So, an important part of simplification involves going through your closet before you make new purchases. This can be a trip down memory lane ("that's the top I bought on that wonderful trip to

Cancun") or the reliving of trauma ("that's what I was wearing when Elbert broke up with me"). Clothes have deep hooks in our emotional history. That's why it's healthy to let go of the things that don't reflect who we are today.

Most personal organizers and fashion advisors suggest going through your closet and throwing away anything you haven't worn in one year. I admit that this one is hard for me—and I bet it is for most of you. In fact, I still hire my shopping adviser, Hella, to help me decide what to let go. And some of the time, I disagree with her! I tend to extend that review to things I haven't worn for at least *two* years, sometimes even three, unless they are expensive classic pieces that can be updated, if necessary, with minor tailoring. Of course there are some things that go out of fashion very quickly and are easy to toss, particularly if you're one of those High Spirited or very fashion-forward types who jump on trends. But I admit that I have held on to some things well beyond their usefulness, and I've regretted it.

That said, something on one of my favorite shows, *What Not to Wear*, really bugs me. One of the hosts will grab a garment, declare it unfit, and toss it in the trash, leaving the guest with a look of longing and helplessness. That seems a bit harsh. I think everyone should be allowed those few (I reiterate, *few*) items that make no sense but have great meaning. (I kept my wedding dress—it's classic and wearable.) If you're a romantic or old-fashioned type you probably have a closet full of cherished memories, perhaps some vintage finds that are real treasures. So I'm not going to address those kinds of items. Keep and protect them: no wire hangers and mothproof them with lavender sachets.

What I'm referring to is that pricey jacket you bought six seasons ago that not only no longer fits you, it no longer fits your lifestyle. The pair of hot pink stiletto sandals, bought on impulse for a vacation that you wore exactly once. And then, of course, anything that looks sad (or makes you sad to look at it), is damaged, or faded beyond your coloring—out! These are the easy discards.

Then there's the more personal stuff. The Audrey Hepburn dress you bought because your then boyfriend thought she was the ideal woman, even though you are really a laid-back earth mother type. The fur coat bequeathed you by your late aunt before you became an ardent vegan. The double-decker platform boots you wore to your first Michael Jackson concert. Vintage gems or albatrosses? Ultimately, only you can make that call. The point is to stay just this side of that fine line between being sentimental and hoarding.

Here's a little keep-it-or-ditch-it checklist:

- *Have I worn or used this item in the last two or three years? (Unless it's a classic it's probably out of style anyway.)*
- *Does the color flatter me or, if it once did, has it faded?*
- *Is the style one that I now know is not mine?*
- *Does it no longer fit me? Can it not be altered to fit?*
- *Does it no longer fit my lifestyle?*
- *Is it no longer age-appropriate?*
- *Does it remind me of a time I'd rather forget or an experience it would be good for me to let go of?*

- *Do I keep it only because it was given by a friend or family member, or cost a lot of money?*

- *Is it dirty, damaged, or irreparable?*

These practical questions will help you purge your closet. Now for the philosophical one that will help you cleanse your soul:

- *Am I willing to create the space for new, wonderful, and appropriate things, experiences, and growth in my life?*

For some of you, seeing your new style facets and revised color palette will be a big change in your life. This is not something to take lightly. We have strong attachments to our clothing and to certain colors because they speak to some part of our conscious or subconscious. So be gentle with yourself when you start purging your closet.

Many of the most notable New Age teachers, including Louise Hay (a personal favorite of mine on this subject) have described the process that takes place when you create a healthy vacuum in your life. Letting go of old junk—inner and outer—makes room for new, good, and positive things to come into your life. So consider donating your clothes to Goodwill, the Salvation Army, a women's shelter or a nonprofit that provides clothing for women entering the workforce. Particularly if it's only a year or two old it will still be useful and bring delight into someone else's life.

If it's an item not worth giving away, you can always use it for housecleaning (which I do with my old T-shirts). If something cannot be given away or repaired, its components can possibly be remade into something else. Recently, a whole slew of sustainable clothing designers have started making new items out of old. An Internet search on recycled clothing can help you find one near you. [Can you tell I'm a recycling fanatic?]

Once you have some space in your closet you will be better able to see what you really need. Shopping for necessities gives you a sense of purpose. It helps you avoid wasteful impulse purchases. The problem with buying on impulse is that you can end up spending a lot of your time and energy trying to fit a new piece into your wardrobe only to find it just doesn't work. Of course, you may serendipitously find something that fits in perfectly, but that will most likely be a result of deep familiarity and comfort with your colors and style. Having an organized closet and a good understanding of your needs makes your shopping experience more meaningful.

Above all, this whole exercise in fashion should be fun! Love everything in your closet and then *wear* everything in your closet. Repeatedly. Get the full value of what you paid for your clothing. We used to describe items saved for special occasions as our Sunday best. But we all have what I like to call the someday best. The thinking process goes like this: "I don't want to get this dirty or be seen in it too frequently because *someday* I'll need it for a really special occasion." Don't save that exceptional thing for a single special event and then find a year or two later that it's out of style—and you've worn it only once. Wear it, use it, flaunt it, and enjoy it as you relish being the fabulous, beautiful, fashionable, and elegant creature you are, today and every day.

Becoming Your Own Stylist

By now I hope you've absorbed enough of this information to see how the elements of color and style reflect who you are as an individual. Understanding your unique color palette and the amount of each style archetype that is reflected in your features, stature, body type and personality are the first steps toward creating a more useful, beautiful and satisfying wardrobe.

But doing so is a skill. And like all skills it requires practice. It also requires that we revisit our colors and style periodically, since changes in our bodies, faces and skin brightness over time, can influence what we look best in and what we want to emphasize.

So here are a few exercises to help test and hone what you have learned.

For the next few weeks notice what people are wearing. Don't stare—just observe. Disregard the fantasy outfits worn by rock stars and celebrities. Just pay attention to people in your own environment, since they more closely reflect the lifestyles, needs, and overall "vibe" of your community. You can do this at the local Starbucks, on the train or bus for your local commute, in line at the bank or supermarket, or at the mall. You can also use this process while thumbing through your favorite magazines and catalogs as those images provide other kinds of challenges and questions to consider.

Then ask yourself:

- *What do I like about what I see (color, style, fit)? Why?*
- *Am I being objective or is my feeling based on my personal taste and color/style?*
- *What strikes me as dissonant? Why?*
- *Do the proportions flatter, enhance, or detract from the person wearing it?*
- *If I could change something they're wearing what would I change? Why?*

This exercise is not only a great training tool it's a valuable way to develop appreciation for people's differences. It helps you see each human being as an individual with unique coloring, style, body shape, and personality.

One of the biggest challenges in shopping and fashion is to separate our own likes and dislikes from simple, objective observation. But it's an extremely valuable skill to develop. And, not only is it a way to appreciate differences among our fellow humans, it is a great tool for shopping. It also helps one develop an eye for some of the principles in art and design.

Now with your more discerning eye, apply the principles you have learned to shopping for your own wardrobe. Ask yourself if any new— or old—item or outfit you're considering complements and enhances your coloring. If it has is a multi-colored pattern, is there one color that jumps out as dissonant with the other colors and/or is unflattering to your own skin tone. Envision the new item hanging in your closet and ask yourself whether it harmonizes with the other pieces that you know work for you.

Notice if the overall style echoes your personality, bone structure and body shape. Then look at the structure of the piece as it appears on your body. If a hemline or some other part of the garment is too long, too short, or if a seam is too tight or too loose, look to see if that is something that can be easily altered to make it fit well. Then, if you are trying on pieces that go together check their proportions to see if they balance each other in a graceful manner.

After a while these processes will become second nature. You'll just know what works or what doesn't and more importantly, why they do or don't work for you. And you will find yourself quickly homing in on items that match your criteria and your needs without wasting a lot of time and money. Another advantage is that you will be less likely to be distracted by the newest thing in the stores if you know it just doesn't work for you.

And best of all, the process is a whole lot of fun! You'll start to feel empowered with the knowledge you have gained. You will be an expert on your own style.

Ultimately all the elements come together to connect your inside with your outside. You project harmony: a physical image that represents all parts of yourself. It's a deeply satisfying process of discovery, one that celebrates the real you.

Once you've done some people watching with these questions in mind, then turn the mirror on yourself

Ask yourself: *Does what I wear make my life simpler, bring me delight, create visual harmony, and express the real me?*

Epilogue

n all my reading, observation, and personal experience I've yet to find one system of color and style analysis that tells the entire story accurately, every time. This is because life, like fashion, is fluid and ever-changing. Many years ago, my sister gave me an important piece of advice: "Never take anyone's advice as gospel—including mine." I reinterpreted that to mean, "Choose your prophets wisely but always seek your own truth." I think that's a good philosophy for life in general and it's very applicable to shopping.

There will be those times when you find something that's maybe not quite in your color range but that fills you with delight. Like that lilac T-shirt (nowhere in my color palette) that just makes me happy. Perhaps you want to experiment with a hairstyle that's a trifle more "romantic" than your usual look. Or with a pair of edgy boots that make you feel a little bit rock 'n' roll. When one of those choices presents itself, I say *go for it!*

The last thing you need when you're honing your personal style is an inner critic telling you not to go a little wild now and then—and not to trust your intuition. When you give yourself permission to break the rules, those wild moments will be joyful. Because you understand the real you, they'll also be fewer and therefore less expensive. Make this your motto:

Train your eye; trust your gut; don't obsess.

It is my hope and belief that by the time you've implemented these rules you will have bloomed into the beautiful being you truly are: colorful, stylish, fresh, elegant, and authentic.

Here's to the Real You!

Acknowledgments

I have been blessed to work with some of the best and the brightest in the field of color and style analysis and the best and brightest of them is John Kitchener, Director of Personal Style Counselors (PSC) in Oakland, California. John brings an extensive art background and a wealth of experience to his work, having seen more than 23,000 clients. To say that his advice changed my life is not an overstatement. I am deeply indebted to him, as are the numerous friends and family members I have sent to his office over the years.

A very special note of gratitude and appreciation goes to the estate of Harriet T. McJimsey—specifically her son Dr. George McJimsey—for granting me permission to use and amend her style-type charts.

Hella Tsaconas, my personal shopper par excellence, read multiple drafts of this book and offered enlightened guidance. Her gentle manner belies a brilliant critical eye. Artist Judy LaMar read early drafts of the style charts and helped me understand my own style.

My sister, Judy Chaikin, continues to inspired me by demonstrating how to have a vision and bring it to fruition.

And then there are my guinea pigs and fellow PSC color and style fans many of whom offered feedback and encouragement and scratched out the time to go over multiple drafts of the material: Dinah Childress, Marilyn Goldhaber, Valerie Janlois, Ellen Jefferds, Maribeth Martell, Jan McCutcheon, Jane McKinne, Elizabeth Morrison, Dayna Norris, Charlotte Sproul and Anna Urrea. Samantha Wallace's expertise in the world of fashion helped me bring clarity and conciseness to the material, and my shopping buddy, Margaret Glazer, always offered an honest, cogent eye.

Two of my most delightful inspirations have been my niece, Sara

Andreas who embraces fashion with a vengeance, and my great-niece Sequoia Chamlee, who at the age of five was already directing sartorial commentary to the TV screen.

Every author heaps praise on her editors and mine deserve a mountain of it. Douglas Gorney, who has ghostwritten the memoirs of Hollywood jailbirds and sports heroes, helped me bring clarity and focus to the first draft. Nancy Sherman's eagle eye broke me of bad punctuation habits in my last-minute edits and took the manuscript through the final version.

My illustrator Susan Tait Porcaro made the process of bringing the material to life a complete and effortless delight from beginning to end. My book designer, Shannon Bodie, offered cheerfulness and flexibility throughout the entire book design process.

And eternal love and gratitude goes to my husband, Pflash. I think the greatest gift any human being can give another is unconditional encouragement and support for their wildest dreams and creative goals. He has given me that in great measure for nearly 25 years.

And to you, dear reader, thank you from the bottom of my heart for buying this book.

Here's to the Real You!

Appendices

Further reading

Art and Fashion in Clothing Selection by Harriet T. McJimsey (Iowa State University Press, 1963) Currently out of print but available online through independent booksellers.

The Arts of Costume and Personal Appearance by Grace Morton (University of Nebraska Foundation, 1943) Currently out of print but available online through independent booksellers.

Color Smart by Mimi Cooper and Arlene Matthews (Pocket Books, 2000) A charming little book that describes the influence and effect of color.

The Pocket Stylist by Kendall Farr (Gotham Books, 2004) Great tips from a fashion insider, particularly for different body types.

Open and Clothed by Andrea Siegel (Agapanthus Books, 1999) An entertaining and profound exploration into the psychological relationship we have with our clothing.

You Can Heal Your Life by Louise Hay (Hay House, 2004) As one of the early human development coaches, Louise has walked the talk for decades. This is a great resource to help you examine and move beyond your inner obstacles to health and happiness.

Transcendental Meditation by Jack Forem (Hay House, 2012) Recently revised to include extensive scientific research, this personal, charming, and wise book explains why TM is unique among meditation techniques and self-help programs and how it can help you become the real you.

Recommended websites

John Kitchener, Personal Style Counselors: (510) 220-3369
(pscjohnkitchener.com) Simply the best color analyst I have found
anywhere.

Hella Tsaconas: hellapersonalstyle.com Has wonderful regular
updates with references to personal style, color and how they
pertain to fashion trends.

The Fashion Fit Formula: www.fashionfitformula.com A terrific
resource to help you identify the most flattering alternation points
for your body.

Campaign for Safe Cosmetics: safecosmetics.com An organization that
deserves our attention and support.

Skin Deep: skindeep.org This site, an offshoot of the Environmental
Working Group, provides an entire encyclopedia of personal care
product ingredients and rates their carcinogenic potential from
1 to 10.

Truth in Aging: truthinaging.com Researcher and beauty expert
Marta Wohrle analyzes all the new "miracle" antiaging products
for their effectiveness and safety. The site also has an extremely
thorough A–Z ingredient analysis.

Shopping Resource Index

The following is a list of some of the most popular clothing catalogs and affordable retailers in the United States with descriptions of the predominant color, style, and fit they routinely carry. The styles are listed in order of the primary style types of their designs. *Note: All these retailers include a variety of colors and styles during different seasons, but certain color palettes and styles predominate and those are reflected here.*

Abercrombie & Fitch
Color: Striking Contrast, Lively Bright
Style: Youthful, Natural
Fit: XS–L

Ann Taylor
Color: Mostly Lively Bright
Style: Classic, Youthful. Great selection of LBDs
Fit: Regular, Petite, and Tall sizes

Anthropologie
Color: Mostly Lively Bright
Style: Youthful, High Spirited
Fit: XS–XL (0–16), Petites 00P–14P

Banana Republic
Color: All color harmonies but mostly Striking Contrast, Lively Bright, and Earthy Rich
Style: Classic and Natural, some Youthful
Fit: Petites 00–14, Regular 00–16, Tall 4–16 online only

Boden
Color: Mostly Lively Bright and Subtle Blended
Style: Natural and Youthful
Fit: 2–18 and Petites

Boston Proper
Color: Mostly Striking Contrast, Lively Bright, and Earthy Rich
Style: Dramatic, Romantic
Fit: 0–18

Burberry
Color: Mostly Striking Contrast and Earthy Rich
Style: Classic, Dramatic
Fit: Women's 0–14

Calvin Klein
Color: All seasons (but emphasis on neutrals)
Style: Classic
Fit: Regular 2–14, XS–XL, Plus 0X–5X; Petites PXS–PL

Chadwicks
Color: Mostly Striking Contrast, Lively Bright, and Subtle Blended
Style: Classic, Youthful
Fit: Regular, Petite, Tall, and Plus sizes S–XL, 4–18

Chico's
Color: All seasons
Style: Dramatic, Natural
Fit: Chico's carries proprietary sizes corresponding to 0–22

Coldwater Creek
Color: Lively Bright and Subtle Blended
Style: Natural, Classic
Fit: Petites PXS–PXL, Women's 1X–3X,
Misses XXS–XL

COS
Color: Striking Contrast, Earthy Rich,
Subtle Blended
Style: Natural, Classic, Dramatic
Fit: 2-14 Regular XS-L

Cuyana
Color: Subtle Blended and Earthy Rich
Style: Classic, Natural
Fit: XS, S, M, L

DKNY
Color: Mostly Striking Contrast and
Earthy Rich
Style: Natural, Dramatic, Romantic
Fit: Women's P–XL; Petites PXS–PL;
Plus 1X–3X and 14–28

Diane von Furstenberg
Color: All seasons
Style: Romantic, Classic
Fit: 0–14, P–L

Eddie Bauer
Color: Mostly Subtle Blended and
Earthy Rich
Style: Natural, Classic
Fit: Standard plus Classic, Easy,
and Shaped pants

Eileen Fisher
Color: Subtle Blended, Earthy Rich, and
some Striking Contrast
Style: Natural, Angelic
Fit: Regular, Petite, and Plus sizes

Everlane
Color: Earthy Rich, Subtle Blended,
Striking Contrast
Style: Natural, Relaxed
Fit: 00–12

Forever 21
Color: Primarily Striking Contrast,
Lively Bright, Some Subtle
Blended, little Earthy Rich
Style: Youthful
Fit: XS–L and Plus XL–3X

Gap
Color: All color harmonies
Style: High Spirited, Youthful, Natural
Fit: XS–XXL; Petite 00P–14P;
Tall 4T–16T

Garnet Hill
Color: Lively Bright, Subtle Blended,
and Earthy Rich
Style: Youthful, Natural
Fit: Standard sizes XS–XL, 2–18

H&M
Color: All color harmonies
Style: All Style types (emphasis on
Classic, Youthful, High Spirited)
Fit: 2–14, XS–XL

J. Crew:
Color: Mostly Lively Bright and Subtle
Blended; some Striking Contrast
Style: Classic, Youthful
Fit: Regular 00–20, Petites 00–14,
and Tall 00–20

J. Jill
Color: Mostly Lively Bright and Subtle
Blended
Style: Natural, Classic, and some
Angelic
Fit: Petite, Misses, Women's
and Tall XS–XL 2–28

Joe Fresh
Color: All color harmonies
Style: Classic, Youthful
Fit: 0–14

Kate Spade
Color: Lively Bright
Style: Youthful, Classic
Fit: 00–14; XXS–XL

Lafayette 148
Color: Mostly Striking Contrast, Lively Bright, and Subtle Blended
Style: Classic, some Youthful
Fit: Regular 0–18, Petite 0–16, and Plus 14W–24W

Land's End
Color: Lively Bright and some Subtle Blended
Style: Natural and Classic, some Youthful prints
Fit: Petite, Misses, Womens XXS (0) through XL (18) and 14W–26W

LLBean
Color: All seasons
Style: Natural, Classic, Youthful
Fit: Petite, Misses, Women's XS–XL 4–20 and 16–26W

Michael Kors
Color: Striking Contrast, Lively Bright, some Earthy Rich
Style: Classic, Dramatic
Fit: XS–XL (2–16), Petite 2–14

Old Navy
Color: All color harmonies
Style: Natural, High Spirited, Youthful
Fit: 00–18, XXS–XXL

Peruvian Connection
Color: Subtle Blended, Earthy Rich, some Striking Contrast
Style: Romantic, Angelic, and Dramatic
Fit: 0–18, XS–XL, some Petites

Poetry
Color: Subtle Blended
Style: Natural

Fit: 2–18, XS–L

Pure
Color: Lively Bright, Subtle Blended, and some Earthy Rich
Style: Natural, Angelic. Large selection of cashmere sweaters and accessories
Fit: 2–18

Ralph Lauren
Color: Mainly Earthy Rich and Striking Contrast; all colors seasonally
Style: Classic, Natural, some Romantic
Fit: Regular XS–XL (0–18) Women's 14–22, Petites 2–14

Sundance
Color: Subtle Blended, Earthy Rich
Style: Natural, Romantic, some Angelic
Fit: XS 2–16 XL 2–16, Petites 2–14

Talbots
Color: Striking Contrast and Lively Bright
Style: Classic
Fit: Misses 2–20, Petites 0–16, Women's 12W–24W, Women's Petite 12WP–22WP

Tommy Hilfiger
Color: Lively Bright and Striking Contrast
Style: Classic, Natural, some High Spirited (preppy)
Fit: Regular, XS–XXL, 0–18

Uniqlo
Color: All color harmonies
Style: Classic, some Youthful
Fit: XS–XXL

Zara
Style: Classic, Natural
Color: All but emphasis on Earthy Rich
Size: 2–14, XXS–XL

Index

About the Author

Photo: Margaret Ryle

Andrea Pflaumer is a Bay Area-based writer and lecturer with a lifelong passion for fashion. For 12 years she was a contributing editor to the *East Bay Monthly* and to *Oakland Magazine* where she wrote their Shop Talk and Shopping Around Features.

Her research into the principles of individual color and style is based on the Personal Style Counselors system, the oldest and most thorough system for custom, individual color palettes and style essence analysis.

Andrea is a regular contributor to numerous national and international fashion, arts and lifestyle publications. She lives in Berkeley California with her husband, Pflash.

You can follow her regular updates and blog posts about fashion trends and how they relate to the real you: ShoppingfortheRealYou.com

67774054R00101

Made in the USA
Lexington, KY
21 September 2017